Leonard Levitt

# AN
# AFRICAN SEASON

JONATHAN CAPE
THIRTY BEDFORD SQUARE LONDON

FIRST PUBLISHED IN GREAT BRITAIN 1968
© 1966, 1967 BY LEONARD LEVITT

To all the Fedsons

PRINTED IN GREAT BRITAIN BY
LOWE AND BRYDONE (PRINTERS) LIMITED, LONDON
ON PAPER MADE BY JOHN DICKINSON & CO. LTD
BOUND BY A. W. BAIN & CO. LTD, LONDON

# PART ONE

# I

THEY TOOK US IN the Land Rover, Mike and me, with Kim Buck driving. We had planned to leave that morning, as it was a good four hours' drive, although it was only about sixty miles from Mbeya. But it had taken us the whole morning just to buy our supplies—tins of paraffin oil, as there was no electricity, they had said, packets of tinned meat and vegetables and fruit and bread, as they weren't exactly sure what the food situation would be like down there, things for the house like chairs and paint and brushes and nails, a hammer, rope, string, soap, a basin, a bucket—all things I would never have thought to buy but that Mike said were necessary. And then trying to fit it all into the Land Rover, with Kim Buck muttering we were going to be late as hell, giving orders which neither of us could understand, to place this inside the door here, no, not there, and that underneath this and this on top of that. . . .

So it wasn't until late that afternoon that we were able to get away, and the tarmac turned to dirt and stones a few miles outside of Mbeya with large potholes all through the road because the short rains had recently begun.

I'd been having some chills and stomach trouble for the last week—because of the water in Mbeya, they had thought, or maybe it was a touch of malaria, they weren't sure—and I began to get those shooting pains which came every afternoon at that time, as we bumped along the dirt road, swerving to avoid the potholes, shooting the little pebbles on the road in all directions like a spray.

The mountains began to rise up on the left, blue with white puffy clouds sitting just above their peaks, while on the right—black-brown fields with furrows. Sometimes you could see a man standing there in the field, with a hoe, only a pair of shorts on his black body. He would stop his work and look up at the Land Rover as we passed, standing in the same place staring after us, becoming smaller and smaller in the distance.

Kim Buck kept glancing down at his watch every few minutes, shaking his head and muttering, We're going to be late as hell. They had prepared a party for us that night at Martin Martinson's. He was one of the English tea planters down there—they're called Europeans. The party was to welcome us, Mike and me, as we were the first new white faces there in a long time, Kim Buck had said, and most of them were leaving now, what with *uhuru*. In fact it was Kim Buck's guess that they would all, all the European planters who still remained, be at the party tonight to meet us.

We were climbing now, the road wiggling in figure eights into the mountains, and Kim Buck had to put the Land Rover into overdrive. And the white clouds above the peaks were changing into a grayish mist that was beginning to creep over the hills in the distance. Tukuyu was the wettest district in the highlands, they had told us, up to 150 inches of rain a year. During the rainy season, Kim Buck said, it would rain for days on end without our ever seeing the sun, and the road that we were on now—which ran from Mbeya to Tukuyu—would become impassable for a good part of the year.

That means you might be quite isolated for a few months, he said to us, so you'd better enjoy yourselves tonight at the party while you still can. And he laughed to himself. Somehow it didn't seem very funny to me.

Occasionally we'd pass clumps of little huts along the side of the road. There would be ten or fifteen of them together, with walls made of mud, and thatched roofs of leaves and twigs, and we could see smoke seeping through the roofs, which probably meant that they were cooking inside. Sometimes there would be a few old men sitting in front of the huts, wearing only a sheet wrapped around them. We'd wave to them as we passed and they'd slowly lift their arms to wave back, but most of the time they would just stare off into space without making a motion.

And we'd pass children standing on bird-thin legs with only a black cloth around their skinny little bodies covering them from their shoulders to their thighs. If they stood near the road you could see how dirty they were with cakes of mud all up and down their arms and legs. Or sometimes you would see great scablike sores and blotches on their faces. We would wave to them, and they would nudge each other and jump up and down, waving their arms and shrieking *Jambo, jambo,* laughing with great white teeth as the Land Rover sprayed pebbles at their bare feet.

And little old men, walking along the side of the road, barefoot, poking with a stick at three or four scraggly old cows. Sometimes if there were more, the cows would stream across the entire road followed by two or three little boys, not more than six or seven years old it seemed, each carrying a little thin stick and wearing only that black cloth. We would have to slow down to pass them, and Kim Buck would lean on his horn, and they would all start in fright. Then the old man would yell at the little boys, who would run at the cows with their sticks, beating them frantically to the side of the road.

It was growing darker now as we raced onto a strip of tarmac, on the right a market with swarms of Africans, and to the left, uphill, another street—ragged wooden buildings on either side, a raised sidewalk in front of the buildings, a wooden railing in front of the sidewalk like a hitching post. It looked something like an old Western town in the movies except that there weren't any horses and all the people were black. Kim Buck said that this was Tukuyu. And then it was gone . . . the dirt road again, with the mountains on the left. Only now they were a heavy gray because the clouds had camped on them and night was coming.

Then farther on we came to a group of huts on the right, and Kim Buck turned the Land Rover down another dirt road, this one so narrow that at first I thought it was only a path. Banana trees on both sides, their thick green leaves reaching across the road and brushing the Land Rover as we drove past. The road was bumpy, bumpier even than the main road, filled with potholes, as we bounced slowly along. And there around the corner lay a large truck turned over on its side. It must have skidded into a pothole when the road was very wet and gone over, strewing large cartons all over the road.

All this without stopping as we joggled our way past. The road forked again and we turned again to the right, the road becoming even narrower than before with huts now on either side and people standing in front of them, staring at us as we passed. Then a sign which said NDUMULU SCHOOL, ½ MILE, and there ahead a large arch built of bricks which were beginning to fall down, and another sign which said ALL VEHICLES GO LEFT AROUND THE ARCH. But it was difficult to read it now in the dusk, so Kim Buck drove straight on underneath the arch, and there inside stood a group of Africans, ten or so, and they fell back into a semicircle as we stopped the Land Rover and stepped out.

They were all wearing slacks and white shirts, very clean, maybe new, and polished shoes. A heavyish tall man with spectacles stepped out of the center and introduced himself as Mr. Biboko, the assistant headmaster. They had been expecting us since morning, he said, but the headmaster had finally decided that we weren't coming today and had this very minute gone to his house. Someone had just gone to call him.

Kim Buck apologized for our being late like this, he hoped we hadn't caused them any inconvenience. Oh no, Mr. Biboko said, and smiled big white teeth, and he began introducing us to the others, who, he said, were teachers at the school, and just then the headmaster trotted up.

He was tall and thin, wiry, athletic-looking, and very black, with a long curling mustache. He was wearing sparkling white shorts and white knee socks like the old pictures of British colonial officers—only you could see a part of his black leg coming through a hole just below the knee—and a blue blazer which was too small for him so that he wasn't able to button it and it flapped around him as he walked.

He was Mr. Thomson Twakatulu, headmaster of Ndumulu School, and he was very sorry for not being there to meet us. As he spoke, he seemed to bounce up and down, and he began leading us away from the others toward a row of little brick houses with corrugated tin roofs, stopping and pointing to two that he said were ours.

How nice, I said. Somehow I had half expected a mud hut like those we had passed on the road.

He told us that our beds and tables and refrigerator had come, and that they had all helped carry them inside our houses.

Thank you, I said, we appreciate it very much. And he began nodding his head very seriously and vigorously, saying, Thank you, thank you.

10

Mike said he was glad to know his bed had come, so we wouldn't have to sleep on the floor. He smiled a little as he said it, and Mr. Twakatulu nodded his head again, saying, Yes, yes, very, very.

Then he said that they had all expected us earlier and that they had been waiting for us since this morning, that they had prepared a welcoming dinner for us, that all the teachers and their wives would be there, and that perhaps Kim Buck would like to come also. But Kim Buck said, No, he couldn't, he didn't have time, that in fact Mike and I actually couldn't come either as we had already made other plans to go to the tea plantation. In fact we were late as it was. Frankly speaking we had only just enough time now to drop off some of our supplies.

Mr. Twakatulu said, Oh, and started to nod his head vigorously again. I'm very sorry, Kim Buck said, I hope you don't mind.

Oh no, said Mr. Twakatulu. They could have the dinner another time, maybe tomorrow, and Kim Buck said, Yes, tomorrow, and Mr. Twakatulu started nodding his head again, saying, Yes, yes very, very, we can have it tomorrow.

But maybe we would be too busy tomorrow, he said suddenly to us, Mike and me.

No, I said, we would be very happy to come tomorrow.

Yes, Kim Buck said, we would come tomorrow, but now we had to get going, and he motioned us to climb into the Land Rover.

So we said goodbye to Mr. Twakatulu, and Kim Buck turned the Land Rover around and we headed back through the arch, past the group of teachers still standing in the same place as when we had come. And I thought of the dinner that Mr. Twakatulu said they had prepared specially for us—which we weren't going to. There he was, still standing in front of our houses where we had left him, in his white shorts and knee socks and his blue blazer.

The teachers looked up at us as we passed, and Kim Buck waved to them. But somehow I couldn't so I looked the other way.

It was nearly nine o'clock when we arrived at Martin Martinson's, and there were people swarming all over his lawn, white people, with a charcoal fire in the middle where steaks were roasting, the coals glowing a soft red in the darkness.

Martin Martinson ran over to us as we climbed out of the Land Rover. He was very short and very fat, with blond hair that fell over his eyes. He was very drunk.

11

You're late, mates, he said to us. Better grab some steaks before they're all gone and then come inside and fix yourselves a drink.

So we walked over to the grill and picked off some steaks, and they were hot and tender and very charcoally, and tasted all the better because I had been eating very little this past week because of my stomach.

Martinson led us inside where people started coming up to us and introducing themselves. They handed me a drink, and we talked, with Ray Charles moaning over the hi-fi, about where I was from and how pleased they were to see us here.

Pity, though, you don't have a car, but no matter, we'll be able to pick you up. We have a nice club, a little on the quiet side these days as so many of us have gone, but there are still enough around for a good bash on Saturday night—and they all laughed. We even have a tennis competition Sunday mornings if you are interested.

They asked if there was anything they could do to help us out— they knew how it could be where we were staying—and we smiled politely, Thank you, not yet anyway, we had just arrived today. And Ray Charles was singing "Georgia on My Mind" and some couples were starting to dance—But how can you dance to Ray Charles?—as someone handed me another drink.

Then I was standing next to a Mrs. Gibson, who was telling me that her husband was the head manager of the tea plantation, and I said, Oh that's nice, and she said, Yes, but they were going back to England at the end of the month. That must be very nice, I said, and she sighed—somewhat wistfully I thought—Yes, but it had been a good life out here.

Could I get her another drink, I said, as I was just getting one for myself, and she handed me her glass.

When I returned she told me again that she was going home at the end of the month, because what with *uhuru* it was only a question of time. Then she said quite suddenly, Is it true that you have come here to help the Africans and to live among them, and I nodded, Yes, it was, and she said, Whatever for, and before I could think of anything to say, she had flipped away, leaving me by myself, so I got myself another drink and went outside to get another steak.

But the steaks were all gone now, so I sipped my drink and walked across the lawn, past people talking and laughing together in little groups, past the road where there was a large open field.

The voices were only a hum now, and there was Ray Charles wailing softly out into the night, the lights of the house casting shadows on the lawn, the little groups of Europeans buzzing together as though it were any suburban lawn party, a barbecue perhaps—not the middle of Africa.

Somehow it seemed hard to believe that I had just come from a place called Ndumulu School, where the teachers stood around in a little semicircle, where there was a man called Mr. Twakatulu who wore white shorts and a blue blazer and white knee socks with a hole in them, who nodded his head and said, Very, very.

So I just stood there in the field across the road, listening to the noises from Martin Martinson's party floating out into the night, wondering if these people had these parties every week, they seemed so *happy* buzzing to each other, so snug in their own gossip, in their own little lives.

Then far off I heard it, so soft that at first I thought I was only imagining it, a deep *thump, thump, thump,* a steady *bum, bum, bum* from somewhere out of the night. A drum, a native drum, from somewhere out of the blackness, almost as though to remind you—in case you were about to forget—that it was really Africa. Africa!

Later Kim Buck said he had been looking all over for me because it looked like rain and he wanted to drive back to Mbeya that night. I told him that it didn't look like rain to me, and he laughed and pushed me gently toward the Land Rover.

Mike was already inside and we started off to the sound of a few drops splattering on the roof of the car. Then suddenly as if out of nowhere it began to pour, and Kim Buck started to curse, only you couldn't hear him very well because of the rain pounding on the car. I thought, My God, it really *is* raining, and Kim Buck was smarter than I thought he was, and I stared out of the window, trying to see where we were going. Only we couldn't see anything, it was coming down so hard, so we just kept driving and driving, the road so narrow that you couldn't be sure it even was a road.

Suddenly Kim Buck stopped the car. Somehow we were in the middle of a great field. Kim Buck started to curse again, this time so loud that you could hear him through the rain, and he turned the Land Rover around and we tried to retrace our tracks. But the rain had covered them, so we just drove between tea bushes as best we could where it looked like a road, Kim Buck stopping the car every

13

few seconds to see if he recognized anything—fat chance of that with this rain—becoming madder and madder because we seemed to be getting off deeper and deeper.

Then suddenly, miraculously, we found ourselves back on the main road, but we were facing the wrong way. So we turned around and started off again, only now there were puddles all over the road, the potholes deeper than before. Then turning off to the right, as the road narrowed, the banana leaves brushing the Land Rover on either side . . . ahead the shape of that large truck.

And somehow it seemed so strange, so eerie, those leaves of the banana trees brushing against the sides of the car, that truck lying on its side like the carcass of a huge dead animal, the entrails of its cartons strewn all over the road. How long had it been there, and what had happened to the driver?

Then the fork off to the right again, the brick arch ahead, only Kim Buck didn't drive through it this time, he just stopped the car and said Good luck to us very solemnly, he probably wouldn't be seeing us for some time—as though we were going off to battle.

We shook hands and climbed down out of the Land Rover, the rain wetting our faces as we started to run in the direction of where we thought our houses were.

·     ·     ·

I awoke the next morning to a rooster crowing outside my house. I stuck my head out the window to see just where he was and found myself staring at his red cockscomb. He had been standing right under my window, howling at the top of his lungs. I made a *fft* sound with my teeth against my lip and he toddled off, and I tried to get back to sleep, but now a group of little children were running and screaming past the house, and then I guess for the first time I realized where I was.

As Mr. Twakatulu had told us yesterday, they had brought our furniture inside, and I had stumbled onto the bed, which was somewhere in the middle of the floor. Now I got up and started to put on my pants, which I had used as a pillow.

Just then I heard a voice say, *Hodi*. That's Swahili for May I come in—just about the only Swahili I knew—and quick I scrambled into my pants. There in the doorway stood Mr. Twakatulu and Mr. Biboko. They were staring at me wide-eyed, and I wasn't quite sure whether it was because of the way I looked, having just zipped

14

into my pants, or because of the way I was looking at them as it was so early in the morning.

But I forced myself to smile, and we shook hands, as though it was the most normal thing to come to my house at—and I glanced down at my watch—6:45. They stood there for a few seconds without saying anything, just feeling uncomfortable I guess and making me feel uncomfortable. Probably Mr. Twakatulu felt embarrassed about our running off last night, I thought. So I smiled again. He asked me where Mr. Malone was—that's Mike—and I said that I didn't think he had gotten up yet, and Mr. Twakatulu nodded his head and said, Yes, yes, very, very.

Then Mr. Biboko said that they had prepared a tea party for us that morning. I thought to myself that it seemed a little early for a tea party, and involuntarily I glanced down at my watch again. But Mr. Twakatulu must have taken it to mean that we had some other place to go, that we were planning to run off again as we had done last night, because he began to say that if we had other plans we didn't have to come, that they could make it another time.

Oh, no, no, I said, we didn't have any plans. That in fact we would be delighted to come to the tea party, we were only sorry we hadn't been able to come last night. And I tried to smile.

Yes, thank you, thank you, he said. They would return for us at eight.

They came at nine. Mike had gotten up by then, and they led us single file along a footpath between our houses. We could see off to the right the big blue mountains, which seemed to rise right out of the ground almost in front of you like a great fortress, while to the left the land suddenly dropped off as though the school were sitting on the edge of a great hill. And there through the trees you could catch a glimpse of the lake, Lake Nyasa, a patch of blue nearly fifty miles away, so blue that you couldn't be sure it wasn't the sky.

We came to a group of brick buildings with tin roofs, like our houses, except that they must have been classrooms because through the open door of one we could see a blackboard. Inside were about ten men standing around and talking together, the teachers from last night, in their clean white shirts and trousers. And some of them were wearing faded black tuxedo coats with very wide lapels of about 1935 vintage. They all stopped talking as we entered the room.

A group of women came in, wearing very bright dresses,

15

oranges, yellows, reds, long, down to their ankles, with their hair cut short like a boy's. Each had a baby tied round her back with a shawl, and carried a tray of food on her head, little cakes, bread, jam, pots of tea. They put their trays down on two long tables that were in the middle of the room and went to a bench at the back. As they sat down I noticed for the first time that they were barefoot.

Then one of them swung her baby around in front of her and suddenly, without any warning, she reached her hand down into her dress and pulled out a big black breast and began feeding her baby right there, in front of all of us. Quickly I turned my eyes away so they wouldn't think I was staring. But no one seemed to notice me; in fact all the women now had pulled their breasts out and were nursing their babies as casually as if they were powdering their noses.

Mr. Twakatulu motioned everyone to sit down and we all took seats on benches that had been placed along both sides of the long table. He stood in front of the room and began speaking—something about All I have in my heart and everything I feel in my soul I give to these two Americans who have come here to help us. Pretty heady stuff. Did he mean Mike and me? Must have come from some book he had read.

He went on, speaking about the school, that in a few days they would be opening for the year, about the teachers who were leaving, the ones we were replacing, how sorry they all were to lose them, while I couldn't help glancing over at the women with their babies, little black heads at the big black breasts. I nudged Mike. Who could these women be?

Then Mr. Biboko stood up and spoke about the same things as Mr. Twakatulu, how glad he was to have us here, only he didn't say any of that rubbish about his heart and his soul. Also I noticed he spoke English much better than Mr. Twakatulu did.

Then one by one the others stood up to speak, only now they were speaking in Swahili so I couldn't understand them, and I began looking around at those women again, but they had all put their breasts back inside their dresses, and some of them had begun to eat those little cakes and fresh rolls. I remembered they had warned us about the food, to make sure it was well-cleaned and well-cooked, especially outside our own homes, because how could we know whose dirty hands had prepared what dirty food. Except

16

that it looked so good, freshly buttered rolls with jam and little cakes, especially since it was after ten o'clock now and I hadn't eaten yet today.

So I started eating like the others, hoping that whosever dirty hands they were, they weren't too dirty, while the speeches went on in Swahili. They seemed to be getting longer and I couldn't understand anything so I just kept eating the cakes and the rolls and drinking cup after cup of tea. I caught two of those ladies staring at me, giggling to each other as I gulped down the food. I felt like winking at them as they stared, but instead I only smiled, because someone might take it the wrong way and then where would I be?

Then Mike nudged me and whispered he thought maybe we should make some kind of a speech since everyone else there had. So he stood up and said, How happy we are to be in Tanganyika, especially at Ndumulu School, because everyone seems so friendly. And he sat down.

Everyone started applauding very loudly, and Mr. Twakatulu stood up and began shaking Mike's hand, and then we were all standing up and shaking hands with all of them, while the women marched out. Mr. Biboko told me that they were all wives of the teachers. And he pointed out his wife, who was the one who had pulled out her breast first.

How strange, I thought. These teachers who all seemed so modern, so Western-looking in their white shirts and trousers and shined shoes, who had been to school, who were educated—how could they have wives that were so—so—well, who dressed this way, barefoot, who nursed their babies in public.

Then as we were all filing out, Mr. Twakatulu asked us if we might like to have dinner at his house tonight if we weren't busy because we hadn't come last night. It sounded as though maybe there was some kind of special custom for new teachers to eat at the headmaster's house, so we said, Yes, we'd be more than happy to, and he smiled and seemed very pleased. He would come for us at seven.

So we said *Asante sana* to everyone, which means thank you very much, and we decided to go back to our houses to see if we couldn't start fixing them up. Except that when I reached my house I suddenly felt very tired and I lay there on the bed in the middle of the room and began to take stock of the situation.

Actually our houses weren't bad at all. Each had two rooms, small, about ten feet by ten, just big enough to hold a bed and a dresser—but then again, we didn't need them any bigger—with another room in the center, even smaller, maybe eight by ten, not really a room, more like a hallway which the door opened into. The floor was cement, but there were some holes and sand because it was beginning to crack. The walls were of hard-packed mud whitewashed on the inside, with planks of wood around the walls like rafters, as though someone had been planning to build a ceiling but that was as far as he had gotten.

From the hall there was another door, which opened into a back yard, really just a small plot of dirt, with a high white wall around it. In one corner was a stone building with a chimney, perhaps a stove or fireplace. Apparently the Africans cooked outside. In the other corner was a room of cubicle size with a small hole at the bottom of the wall, maybe for water to run out—a kind of bathing room perhaps. But no running water. How did they wash themselves? And next to it another small room with a door. Opening it . . . *whew,* what a smell inside. It was the *choo*—that's toilet in Swahili—only a hole in the ground so we'd have to squat. And millions of flies buzzing down that hole, where the smell was coming from. God, we'd have to do something about that smell!

They had sent us a refrigerator and a stove, which worked by paraffin oil as there was no electricity—that's why we had brought so many tins. But it was just the parts, they weren't put together. We were supposed to do that ourselves.

Now Mike came in and said maybe he'd start with the stove and the fridge, and that maybe I could start cleaning the floor. So I hunted up the bucket we had brought, and the teacher who lived next door to us, Mr. Mwadunda, said that the water pump was down past where the classrooms were.

I went off down there, and near the pump was a large open field with goalposts at either end—for soccer, their national sport, they had told us—with very short grass, as though it had recently been cut. In the middle of the field, munching on this grass, were some scraggly old cows, and two little boys not more than six or seven years old, in torn, ragged shirts, just like the ones we had seen on the road, each with a little stick. Seeing me, they became very still and stared at me intently as I filled my bucket. When I turned toward them again they had come closer, creeping up to me when my back was turned as though I were some great white animal they had never seen before.

Then I had to carry the bucket back to the house and I was all right for the first hundred yards, but then I'd have to stop about every thirty seconds or so to rest and switch hands.

Mike was still working on the stove as I got down on my hands and knees and began to scrub. I scrubbed and scrubbed, and when my right arm was tired I'd scrub with my left, and when the left was tired I'd scrub with my right, and when both of them were tired I'd just sort of dawdle around and feel sorry for myself.

Soon I had to go and fill the bucket again and I was nearly exhausted this time when I reached the house. Mike announced that he had finally gotten the stove started and that he would begin on the fridge, and I started on another room, down on my hands and knees again, scrubbing, hearing him pounding and clanging at pieces.

Late afternoon, we were still working as the sky started frowning gray behind the blue mountains. Soon the gray had crept across the whole sky, a drop of rain splashed on the tin roof, another and another, and suddenly, a gust of wind and the sound of pebbles bouncing on the roof. The rain! The whole house was shaking as though it might blow down any minute.

I sat down on the floor and looked at my dirty, blackened arms and felt my grimy, sweaty neck. And peering out through the window into the gray I suddenly had this great idea—that I would wash outside in the pouring rain. That's how hard it was coming down. So I pulled off my clothes and grabbed a cake of soap—good old Mike, I never would have thought to bring it—and stepped out into the back yard, the high white wall and the gray sky around me, the cold wet rain whipping my body. And standing under the edge of the roof to catch a strong stream of water that was running off, my teeth starting to chatter as the wind whistled through me, I thought of a poem I had read by Langston Hughes, something about Africa, a black girl, washing herself in the rain, white soapsuds in her black hair. There was something romantic, almost beautiful, about that poem. But there was nothing romantic about me, clutching my white shoulders in the gray wind and the cold, wet rain, scrubbing furiously under the edge of the tin roof at the black smudges of Ndumulu School floor.

·   ·   ·

Mr. Twakatulu came for us at seven. We walked down the path in front of our houses and turned down another path, and there was his house, the same as ours except that his middle room was large and he used it as a living room. There was a table with a hurricane lamp burning, and a man sitting there. Mr. Twakatulu introduced him to us as Mr. Mwambigila, another new teacher. He was very short and very thin, and he reminded me of a little boy.

A very large, heavy woman, wearing a bright yellow dress and no shoes, waddled into the room. She was carrying a tray of food on her head, and she bent down, placing the dishes of food on the table. She came to Mr. Mwambigila and knelt down on the floor in a kind of bow, extending her hand to him and turning her face away at the same time, and said something that sounded like *Oogonile*—with the accent on the *ni*. Mr. Mwambigila touched her hand gently with his and said *Oogonile,* back to her. Then she said *Daga,* and so did he, *Daga,* and they began answering each other, repeating words—or were they mere sounds?—in almost a kind of chant.

She came to me and knelt down on the floor again the way she had to Mr. Mwambigila, extending her hand and turning her face as she said *Oogonile.* I remembered what Mr. Mwambigila had said, so I said *Oogonile* back to her as I touched her hand. And she said *Daga,* so I said it back to her, *Daga.* Then she started some other stuff which of course I didn't understand, and I smiled and said, Whoa, not so fast, and with this Mr. Twakatulu and Mr. Mwambigila burst into a great guffaw, appearing to shake hands but instead slapping each other's palms while I sat there doing my best to smile but feeling extremely foolish.

Mr. Twakatulu explained that this was his wife and that she was welcoming me in Kinyakusa, which is the local tribal dialect, so I told him to thank her very much.

Mrs. Twakatulu went out, returning with plates and four spoons, as Mr. Twakatulu took the covers off the dishes on the table. Chicken and a large bowl of fluffy white rice and another plate of some kind of vegetable.

Mr. Twakatulu and Mr. Mwambigila started shoveling the food onto their plates, taking the pieces of chicken with their hands and stuffing them into their mouths. And since we were very hungry, Mike and I, as we hadn't eaten since the tea party, we also started shoveling it onto our plates and swallowing it as fast as we could. It was all delicious, especially the chicken, soft and salty, except that

20

it was very spicy and very hot and my eyes started to tear. But I kept at it, as Mr. Twakatulu and Mr. Mwambigila smiled appreciatively to each other, seeing the way we were pouring down the food. They said that they thought we liked African food very much, and as our mouths were full we could only nod our heads and grunt Uh-huh.

Mrs. Twakatulu returned now, holding a baby in her arms, and her large body fell into a chair in the corner. The baby started crying, and she flicked her breast out of her dress in one deft motion, just as they had all done this morning. It was a very large breast and very black—ah, what a mother she must be!—and the baby started drawing on it as we went on eating, with neither Mr. Twakatulu nor Mr. Mwambigila appearing to take any notice, while I tried not to peek a look over at her.

When we had finished, two young girls, about ten or eleven, came in and placed a pitcher of water on the table. We remembered to say, No, that we weren't thirsty, because they had warned us to be extra careful about drinking the water. The girls started clearing the table, and Mr. Twakatulu told us that they were his children. He spoke to them and they came over to us, kneeling down and saying *Shikamoo,* which is a Swahili greeting showing great respect. Then they brought in some bottles of beer and placed them on the table, with four glasses, one for each of us, except that Mr. Twakatulu didn't take one himself. He said he didn't like the taste of beer.

The girls went and sat down next to their mother in the corner as Mr. Twakatulu turned the lamp down because he said he didn't want to waste the paraffin. And the beer was good, a little warm, but I was thirsty after the meal and I drank long. When it was finished they brought me another one.

The room was dark now with just a little light from the lamp and we could see our shadows on the wall. There in the corner sat Mrs. Twakatulu with her three children wrapped around her, the baby at the breast, you could hear him drawing at it, making soft sucking noises.

Then a splatter on the roof, and another, and another. The rain had begun again, the sound of pebbles dropping on the roof, banging, shaking the whole house, drowning out all other sounds. A flash of lightning through the window, a clap of thunder. The baby began to cry. Another flash, lighting up the whole room. Mrs.

Twakatulu in the corner like great mother earth, drawing her children into the folds of her body, the four of us around the table in the semi-black room, our shadows flickering on the wall from the low-burning lamp. . . .

Then I had to move my chair because the rain was trickling down through a hole in the roof and landing on my head.

. . .

Mr. Twakatulu was at our house the next morning. He was going to Ushirika. Did we want to go with him? Ushirika was the turnoff on the main road, he said, about two miles away. There was a market and some stores, perhaps we would like to buy something. Mr. Mwadunda, our next-door neighbor, was coming also.

So we began our walk to Ushirika. Only we didn't go very quickly because every few steps, it seemed, Mr. Twakatulu or Mr. Mwadunda would meet some friend of his who was walking on the road, and they would stand there and do the same kind of chant that Mr. Twakatulu's wife had done with Mr. Mwambigila last night, coming together and bending their knees in a kind of bow, shaking hands or rather touching hands very lightly, as the first would say *Oogonile,* which Mr. Twakatulu explained meant something like How are you. The second would say *Oogonile* back, and then the first would say *Ndaga*—there was an *n* at the beginning which I hadn't caught last night—which means Thank you, and the second would say *Ndaga* back to him. Then the first would say *Oowombile,* which is about the same as *Oogonile* except that you would only say *Oowombile* after you had already said *Oogonile,* Mr. Twakatulu explained, and the second answering *Oowombile.* Then the first says *Eh nah,* which is another kind of thank you, and they go on their way.

And it's all said very softly and gently.

*Oogonile*
*Oogonile*

*Ndaga*
*Ndaga*

*Oowombile*
*Oowombile*

*Eh nah.*

And the last *Eh nah* is almost sung.

We went on, stopping with nearly every person on the road, it seemed, old men in trousers with a sheet wrapped around them, barefoot, holding a walking stick; women in bright long dresses down to their ankles, their hair cut short like a boy's, like the wives of the teachers. Mr. Twakatulu explained that they were all returning home from church as it was Sunday and most of the people here were Christians.

The old men would look questioningly at us as we passed, the two white strangers, what were we doing here in this road with two Africans? Mr. Twakatulu would explain to them that we were the two American teachers who had come to the school, and the old men would nod their heads very solemnly to show that they had understood. Then they would say to us, Mike and me, *Ndaga fidyo*, which Mr. Twakatulu told us means Thank you very much.

Further on I tried calling out *Oogonile* to a little old man as he passed on the other side of the road. He stopped in his tracks and involuntarily threw his hands up over his head. Then he ran over to us, taking my hand in both of his, saying *Ndaga, ndaga, ndaga*, and I couldn't help smiling at him, he seemed so happy. He said *Ndaga, ndaga, ndaga* again and began speaking very quickly to Mr. Twakatulu and Mr. Mwadunda, pointing to Mike and me and nodding his head very vigorously, smiling a toothless grin, showing pink-black gums.

Mr. Twakatulu said he was very pleased that we knew Kinyakusa and we all laughed.

Then we were at Ushirika, which is really nothing more than a few little wooden stores and groups of mud huts like the kind we had seen on the road with Kim Buck. But they were so small it didn't seem that anyone could live in them.

Mr. Twakatulu led us into one of the little wooden stores. Inside were things like tinned goods and soap and matches, bright colored shirts and hats, bags of tea and sugar. Mr. Mwadunda looked through the shirts and Mr. Twakatulu fingered the hats. They asked us, Mike and me, if perhaps we wanted to buy something, a shirt maybe or a hat, but we smiled No, thank you.

So they led us back outside, and now there was a crowd of people who became very quiet as we passed. I could sense them following us with their eyes. It gave me a funny feeling.

We crossed the road over to an open patch of dirt where some little old women were sitting on the ground, squatting on their heels, each wrapped in an old cloth, each with a basket of some different food—beans, bananas, rice. Mr. Twakatulu bent down over some red beans, letting them sift through his fingers, while I wondered whether I could eat this food without becoming sick. Then he put some into a bag and gave the woman a coin, and looked up at us. Would we like some beans?

No, thank you, we smiled. No sense looking for trouble.

Then they asked us if perhaps we wanted a drink. I thought they might be offended if we said no again, as we had said no in the store and no to the food, so we let them lead us across the street to a mud hut with a painted sign outside which said TANGANYIKA HOTEL, and underneath it, DANIEL MWAMATUMA, PROPRIETOR. Proprietor. Where'd they ever get that word?

Inside was a hard mud floor with some benches placed around the wall. In a corner, four old men—very old with deep furrowed wrinkles—sat at a table with a bowl of some kind of liquid which they were passing back and forth to each other, each man drinking deeply and solemnly in turn. They wore old trousers and black tuxedo coats like those the teachers had worn yesterday at the tea party, and one of them had a large white turban wrapped around his head. And you could see their bare feet sticking out under the table, hard, flat, like slabs of wood.

Mr. Mwadunda said that they were drinking pombe, which is native beer made from maize that has fermented. The villagers prepared it themselves in their homes, he said, and sold it for two shillings a bowl—about thirty cents.

We sat down and the old men seemed to notice us for the first time. They stopped talking and just sat there, staring at us. No doubt they had never seen white people in here before. Another man entered from the back of the hut and Mr. Twakatulu and Mr. Mwadunda stood up and said *Oogonile* and *Ndaga* to him. This was Mr. Daniel Mwamatuma, they told us, the proprietor. Proprietor. And strangely enough—or maybe not so strangely—he looked like all the bartenders I had seen in my life, with a big stomach and a mustache. And he gave us a big smile and said, *Karibu, karibu,* which means welcome in Swahili.

Mr. Mwadunda ordered beer for all of us. But Mr. Twakatulu said, No, he would have a Coke, and I remembered that he had said he didn't like the taste of beer.

24

Then the old man with the white turban walked over to us and began speaking in very quiet and confidential tones to Mr. Twakatulu, nodding his head as Mr. Twakatulu answered him. Mr. Twakatulu said to us that this man was Bwana Mbulu, that he was one of the local chiefs, and that he wanted to meet us. So we stood up and said *Oogonile* to him and his face suddenly lit up and I thought his wrinkles were going to split. He said something to Mr. Twakatulu and they both laughed.

Mr. Twakatulu said to us, Bwana Mbulu says you both know Kinyakusa, and we all laughed at that. He said that Bwana Mbulu thanked us very much for coming, so we said to thank him too. Then the three other men came over to us and we said *Oogonile* to them one at a time as they all began smiling, *oogonile*-ing and *ndaga*-ing to us, laughing to each other as they returned to their bowl.

A girl came in with our drinks, wearing an old brown-gray dress with a fat, hand-sized hole in the back. Her hair was cut short like a boy's—it seemed to be the way they all wore it—and she put the drinks down on the table, bending her knees and saying *Oogonile* to Mr. Twakatulu and Mr. Mwadunda in a soft voice, looking shyly away from them as she spoke. I guess I noticed her then for the first time, there was something about her, her face maybe, the way she looked away from them. She was only about eighteen or nineteen, and Mr. Twakatulu said that her name was Agnes and that she was Daniel Mwamatuma's daughter.

People were coming to the hut now, standing only a few seconds in the doorway, peeping in at us and moving quietly away as others took their place. Mr. Twakatulu said he was just going across the street to see someone, he would be right back.

So we sat and worked on our beers as Agnes returned, holding a baby, and sat down on a bench against the wall. When I looked at her again the baby was sucking on her breast, which she was cupping in her hand outside her dress, a fine soft brown breast. I asked Mr. Mwadunda if that was her baby, because she seemed like such a young girl.

Yes, he nodded, and that she had another baby also, that she was a very wicked girl, and he laughed. Then he said he was going to find Mr. Twakatulu, he would be right back.

So it was just Mike and me now, with nothing to do but order another beer, and I glanced back at Agnes. The baby was still sucking at her breast and she was drinking from a bowl at the same time. That beautiful brown breast. God, it was unfair to do that to me.

There were more people filling the doorway now, just to catch a glimpse of us, and they would whisper to themselves, pointing at us and laughing. It made us so damn uncomfortable and embarrassed, as though we were on display, but what can you do?

So we just sat there trying to seem interested in our beer, wishing that Mr. Twakatulu and Mr. Mwadunda would come back. At least with them it wouldn't be so bad. Only they didn't come back and our beers lay empty on the table now, time was passing, it was becoming late. And finally we decided that they weren't coming back at all and we got up to leave. We would have to hurry back to school, as the sky was clouding over now with the afternoon rains.

Only now it seemed everywhere along the road people would stop and call *Oogonile* to us and we would call back *Oogonile, ndaga,* only the more people to whom we said *oogonile,* the more other people would be calling *oogonile* to us. They would stop walking as they spoke to us now, so we would have to stop and touch hands, and others, seeing us stopping and saying these greetings, would say it to us too, *Oogonile, ndaga.*

So there we were on the road from Ushirika, with the darkening skies, fumbling with some strange new words which sounded as though they came out of a children's book, *oogonile, ndaga,* with nothing to do but continue repeating them to every person that stopped us, *oogonile, ndaga,* as if it were some kind of mad game, *oogonile, oogonile, ndaga, ndaga, oowombile, oowombile, eh nah.*

Then the rain came, hard, and the wind, and the people scattered like ants, and we went and stood under a thick green leaf of one of the banana trees on the side of the road. Suddenly an old man appeared, that same old man with the white turban, Bwana Mbulu, and tugged at my sleeve. For a moment I wasn't sure what he wanted, but Mike understood, he wanted us to follow him.

He led us off the road through a row of banana trees so thick that we could see nothing in front of us but those green leaves, and although the rain was pouring down, we were hardly getting wet.

Then we were at a clearing. There were three houses of mud with thatched roofs, two smaller ones and a long house that ran the entire length of the clearing, the thatched roof so low that it swept down almost to the ground. Bwana Mbulu led us toward it through an opening that served as a door, and you had to bend very low to enter so as not to hit your head.

Inside it was nearly pitch-dark, only a fire in the center of the floor. I could make out forms of men sitting together on the ground in groups around the hut, each group of men with its own bowl of pombe, passing it around to each other as we had seen Bwana Mbulu and his friends doing at Daniel Mwamatuma's.

Bwana Mbulu led us over to one group that was seated at the far corner of the hut—four of them, very old men with their faces unshaven, wearing baggy trousers with sheets wrapped around them. They all stood up as we approached—they were barefoot— and as Bwana Mbulu spoke to them, they nodded their heads very solemnly.

They were smiling now, two of them with no teeth, just black gums, shaking hands with us, as we shook hands all around. *Oogonile, ndaga.* Bwana Mbulu motioned for us to sit down, so we were in a small circle now, the four of them, Bwana Mbulu with his white turban, and Mike and I.

Their bowl of pombe was nearly empty, only some black seedlike dregs at the bottom. A little old lady appeared with only a blanket around her little body, with large bare feet. On her head she carried a big tin of paint. What could she be doing with a tin like that?

She knelt down, taking the tin off her head, and began pouring from it into the empty pombe bowl a thick mushy gray-brown paste, with bubbles and foam. And as she poured, it suddenly occurred to me what she was doing, what this was all about. It was their pombe she was pouring, they must keep it in these tins.

Bwana Mbulu took the bowl, bubbling, foaming, and placed it down in front of me, and looked at me and said in English, Drink.

I felt my stomach dropping down to my toes. My God, how could I drink that stuff? It wasn't even that we weren't supposed to drink it—if there was one thing they had warned us about over and over, it was never, never to drink the native beer. But not even that, it just *looked* so awful, almost like mud. How could I possibly drink it?

I was conscious that they were all watching me, I didn't see what I could possibly do, so I lifted it up to my mouth, the foam tickling my nose, it smelled like nothing I had ever smelled before. I could see it bubbling, those black seedlike things floating there on top like dead ants. It reminded me of witches' brew, double, double toil and trouble.

Then I closed my eyes and tasted it, like nothing I had ever tasted before—mud with sugar is about the closest I can come to describing it. But somehow I got it down, not much, but enough I thought, and I started to put the bowl down, feeling very much relieved, when Bwana Mbulu said again, Drink.

Oh, no, not again, this was asking too much, not a second time. But I didn't want him to think I actually didn't like his pombe, so I lifted it again, closed my eyes, and took a good swallow, keeping a straight face as best I could, feeling it run through me, down my throat and chest, and gurgle into my stomach.

Then they handed it to Mike. Now it was his turn, the poor guy, but he picked it up without even batting an eyelash, bringing it to his mouth and taking a great big swallow. Then another one, the bastard, as if he were really enjoying it. And when he finished he breathed, Ahhh, very deeply and wagged his head as if to say, Boy, that was sure a treat, while the old men nodded to each other, solemnly and approvingly.

They began passing it around to each other now, each man drinking deeply in turn and wiping his mouth with his sheet when he finished, because it would stick to your lips and to your face if you happened to drink it too quickly and spilled any of it on you. Then it was my turn again and I tried to do better than before, drinking deeply, trying my best to act as if I were enjoying it. I even tried to say Ahh at the end, the way Mike had, only I belched instead, and the old men smiled approvingly—or was it indulgently?

Now other men from other groups started coming over to us, shaking hands, *Oogonile,* and we would stand up, *Oogonile, ndaga,* as they faded back into the shadows of the hut. I thought of these old men sitting there in their sheets, drinking their native beer by the light of the fire on their mud floor, as they had for generations —for how many generations?—into the past.

Suddenly I could hear music. It must be a radio, but where was it coming from? Someone must have a little transistor with him here in the hut. It was Elvis Presley and he was singing:

> *It's down on the end of lo-onely street,*
> *It's . . . Heartbreak Hotel.*

And somehow that radio sounded so grotesque—these natives in their torn old half clothes, in their mud hut, drinking their native beer to the hiccups of Elvis Presley—*and the nights are so lonely, baby* . . . That radio, transforming the mystique of the mud hut into just a hut of mud, these old natives metamorphosing into poor old men, toothless, barefoot, their native concoction evaporating into a dirty, unsanitary liquid from which, no doubt, I would contract a good case of dysentery the next morning.

.     .     .

We didn't get home until late that night. Not that we hadn't wanted to leave earlier, but each time we had moved to go, they had seemed so hurt, as though we just couldn't get up and leave them sitting there by themselves, while the little old woman had come back again and again to fill the bowl. But finally they had told us that all the pombe was finished for today, but that we could come back tomorrow if we would like, there was sure to be some more then.

Now in the darkness of my house we began struggling with the pressure lamps that they had given us. Actually there was nothing very difficult about it once you got the hang of the directions, only pulling out the glass and tying in the mantle. The only trick was to wait about a minute or two after you lit it before you started pumping, because if you pumped too soon the flame would start shooting through the top as though the whole lamp were going to shatter any minute, and you'd have to let the pressure escape and then start all over again.

Finally we heard the sweet little pop sound—it had caught—and the room lit up, bright as electricity. And there up on the walls sat the most gigantic spiders I had ever seen, black with long strawlike legs. They seemed to come from out of the woodwork, those planks that had been put into the wall for the ceiling that no one had ever gotten around to finishing. They would crawl around between the wood and the wall, darting in and out after an unfortunate insect that might be dreaming idly close by. Or they would lie there behind the wood, and all you could see sticking out, just coming through the bottom of the plank . . . a long skinny black leg.

I made sure to keep my bed in the middle of the room when I went to sleep, just in case one of them happened to fall on me. And just as I was dozing off I heard something like the rushing of wings and a pitter-patter of little feet running up and down the walls. Quick I jumped out of bed and ran over to get Mike—he was much better at these things than I was.

Outside we could see what looked like the outlines of little birds flying and perching at the edge of my house, just under the roof. And then a weird, high-pitched *beep-beep* sound, almost like radar. Mike said he knew what it was now, it wasn't birds, it was bats.

Spiders and bats. What kind of house had they given me?

. . .

We spent the rest of the week putting the house into working order. We finally got the fridge and stove running right—they always seemed to be leaking paraffin for some reason or other. We built a little seat for the *choo* so we wouldn't have to squat right over the hole. It was just that smell. We'd have to do something about that soon. We found a rusty old bucket that leaked and tied it to a beam about ten feet high in that outside cubicle, so that you could pour water into it and stand under it, the water dripping on your shoulders or back, depending on how you stood, because there were only two streams of water. I think you could charitably call it a miniature shower.

We made the second room of my house into a kitchen and the second in Mike's into a reading room-living room, building a little bookcase out of some bricks and planks of wood that we found lying around. And villagers were coming to our houses every day, bringing things they wanted to sell, old chairs, cushions, straw mats for the floor, all things we could use. Two people carried a cupboard on their backs I don't know for how many miles, so we bought that too.

I even climbed up on the rafters with a broom handle, into the corners of the roof where the bats were coming in. Part of the bricks had crumbled, I saw, and the bats could squeeze themselves in through the cracks and run around in the corners of the roof. Balancing myself precariously, I'd peer into the corners, poking with the stick, listening for the little pitter-patter. Sometimes I'd see a black, ratlike thing crawling around. I'd swipe at it and occasionally I'd hit one and it would fall to the floor dead. I would examine it, turning it over with my stick—I never wanted to touch them—about six inches long and if you pulled at its wings they

30

would spread to about a foot. With one tooth in the middle of its mouth like a pugnacious, buck-toothed kid.

I found an old ladder down by the pump and climbed up on the outside of the house, filling in the holes in the bricks with patches of mud and little stones so that the bats couldn't get in. And I might have quiet and peace for about three to four weeks. But then they would start again, the *beep-beeps,* and the little pitter-patter— they had found another hole in the wall to enter. One night they were even flying around the room. Another night there were two in my bed, and there was nothing to do but clobber them with a stick —I kept one handy for such emergencies—and then change the sheets, of course, climb up on the rafters again and flush them out, and then up on the ladder outside the next day to fill in the holes.

Occasionally some teachers might pass as I stood on the ladder. They would ask me what I was doing and I would tell them, Bats.

Bats, they would nod to each other. Yes, they knew about the bats, they had them in their houses, very troublesome. And they went off laughing to each other.

We did our own cooking, drawing the water from the pump, boiling for drinking but not for dishes, which we washed in my back yard in the afternoon. Mr. Mwadunda, seeing us one day, asked when we were going to get a servant. We smiled politely back at him—he probably had never seen white people who lived without servants—but he said, No, you must, that they all had wives and daughters to cook and wash and clean, and he had a girl who came in from one of the villages every day to help his wife with chopping wood and grinding maize. What would we do when school began, when we didn't have time to do this work? Who was going to cook for us then? Who was going to wash our clothes and clean the house?

I wondered if he really meant it, or if he was just saying this because we were white and strangers. Except that I did have a large pile of dirty clothes accumulated, and I was getting tired of eating tinned corned beef. Somehow when you think of Africa you never seem to think about who will wash your shirts and shorts, and who will mend your socks.

By Saturday we were out of food. That morning we had eaten our last piece of bread and finished our last tin. That meant Tu-kuyu, which was only seven miles away, Mr. Mwadunda said. If nothing else we could replenish our food supply. Maybe we could even buy something to clean up the smell in the *choo*.

So we began walking to Ushirika, where Mr. Mwadunda said there was a bus that passed at nine o'clock. People in their huts on the side of the road, seeing us pass, would call out to us, *Oogonile* —it sounded soft and pleasant early in the morning—and we would call back, *Oogonile*. Then a long line of *Oogoniles* followed, other villagers in other huts farther down the road. *Oogonile, ndaga, oowombile,* as we *eh nah*-ed our way to Ushirika.

There they told us that the bus hadn't arrived yet, that it was usually late these days because of the rains. In fact it probably wouldn't arrive for another hour or so. And I wondered why Mr. Mwadunda hadn't told us that. So we just stood around in front of Mwamatuma's—that was where the bus stopped, they told us— and a group of people came up to us with their *oogoniles* and *ndagas*. After they said it they would stand back a few feet, staring at us in little groups, holding hands with each other, men holding hands, not with women but with each other. They had told us about this, about the men, not that there was anything funny about it, they just held hands because they were friends, not even holding hands really but touching ever so lightly.

Then a new group would come up, *Oogonile, ndaga*. And after a while it didn't seem so soft and pleasant any more, just kind of tedious, *oogonile, ndaga, ndaga, oogonile*. So we decided that maybe we would walk a little of the way and stop the bus on the road if it came. Or better, some car might pass and stop for us.

There were many other people on the road: women in bright-colored dresses with loads on their heads, just looking straight ahead, moving with a slow grace, their arms swinging at their sides, the loads sitting on their heads as snugly as if they were wearing them as hats; younger men on bicycles, in trousers and sport shirts, zigzagging across the road to avoid the potholes; little old men in ragged shorts and torn shirts, some with nothing but a sheet wrapped around them, with spindly legs, all of them barefoot. They looked so funny in those skimpy shorts without shoes, almost like little children except that they moved so slowly.

They would pass in both directions, never stopping, following each other as far as the eye could see, coming from where I did not know and going to where I could not say, but as steady, as continuous, as a line of ants.

32

And little children by the side of the road, wearing a cloth, standing with their little sisters and brothers who could hardly walk, with only a shirt, nothing for bottoms. They would point to us, Mike and me, as we passed, running along the side of the road in and out of the banana trees, keeping abreast of us, leaving their littler brothers and sisters behind, shouting *mzungu, mzungu,* which is Swahili for white man. Hearing those cries, people would step out of their mud houses along the side of the road, half hidden amid the banana trees. We would call out *Oogonile* to them and they would answer, all in a chorus, *Oogonile,* smiling and laughing to each other, hearing us speak Kinyakusa. Then they would call out other words in Kinyakusa to us, which of course we couldn't understand, so we would just laugh and call back *Ndaga,* which seemed to cover many things.

The blue mountains were on the right now, and through them sometimes you could catch a glimpse of the lake, sitting down there almost fifty miles away. And the sun was beginning to get hot, and no car as yet in sight. It was much easier to say seven miles—it takes about a second—than it was to walk it.

Then there was a faint noise in the distance, a swirl of dust far down the road, an old black car now bumping into view as we started pumping our hands up and down because that is the way you do it in East Africa.

The car was making an awful noise, and it skidded to a stop a few feet in front of us. It was an African. Yes, he was going to Tukuyu. How is Ndumulu School? he asked us as we climbed in.

Fine, I said, wondering how he knew who we were.

He had heard about us at Ushirika last week, he said, as we settled back into the seat, the car jiggling along over the bumps and potholes between the endless lines of people along both sides of the road.

Then we were in Tukuyu. He said he would let us off at the marketplace, pointing just to the left where there were some stalls with people selling food. He would probably be seeing us again at Ushirika, he added, he came there every Sunday.

We got out and walked past the market. We could see now that the stalls were just the front, that the real market stretched far behind into an open field, with the women sitting in their rags, squatting on their haunches, their baskets in front of them, their food—eggs, tomatoes, onions—placed in rows on the ground.

B

33

The sun was hot and beat down on the old women as little naked children ran among them, crying, stepping on the food with their hard bare feet. And the smell of sweat, the flies swarming through the market, lighting on the food and on all of them sitting there in the sun. . . . I recalled when we had passed here with Kim Buck in the Land Rover when Tukuyu had been just a blink and it was past. How different it seemed now.

We turned to the right where the street ran uphill. On the raised sidewalk were little wooden stores, and inside Indians—they had told us that Indians control all the trade of East Africa—standing behind their counters, tan skins and sharp features, in trousers, with clean, white sport shirts and new shoes. And Indian women, wrapped in saris, long gowns that fell to the floor, with big bodies and very black hair pulled tight in a bun, black-brown eyes with a red, jewel-like dot on their foreheads.

We walked on and suddenly there was a white lady directly in front of us.

She looked dainty and clean in a white dress. You must be the new Americans, she said to us, extending a little hand.

Yes, I said.

Yes, she said, I'm so pleased to meet you both.

She told us how sorry she was to have missed meeting us at Martin Martinson's. I wasn't sure whether she meant she had not been at Martinson's or whether she had been there but had not met us.

But no matter, she went on. We can get acquainted today. How would we like a good English meal? And before we had realized it, she had deposited us in her car, saying that her house was just outside of town, only a minute's drive.

We turned into a long, lean driveway with well-marshaled shrubs to a flowing green lawn and a large house set back under stately, shady trees. There on the lawn was a large man wearing white shorts and knee socks and a blue blazer. He was prancing up and down like a prize animal, and I couldn't help thinking of Mr. Twakatulu with his white shorts and knee socks that had the hole in them, with his blazer that flapped around him as he walked.

We got out of the car and the lady led us over to him. She said he was Mr. Stark, her husband, and then to me very sternly, What is your name, young man? And yours? turning to Mike. She told her husband that we were the two new Americans they had heard about, whom they were to have met at Martin Martinson's.

She explained to him how she wanted these boys to have a good English meal, as God knows what we must be eating out there. He nodded and said, Mm-hmm, and to us, Come along with me, as he led us to the edge of his lawn, which was on the top of a hill.

Look around from here, he said. There were the blue mountains almost hanging over us as though the house were nestled among their folds. Quite a sight.

Quite a sight, he said, as if he were reading my mind.

He led us inside and sat us down in the living room and poured out some Scotch—they called it whisky. Mrs. Stark came in and he poured her a drink. Then an African in a white jacket and bow tie entered the room. *Tayari,* he said, which means ready in Swahili. I thought he must mean the food, but Mrs. Stark said to us, Your bath is ready if you care to take one, and I looked at Mike. I couldn't believe my ears. A bath! This wonderful woman.

Mike went in first, and they started talking to me about how things were out there, as though I were thousands of miles from Tukuyu, not just seven. She said, How terribly lonely and frustrating it must get, but I explained that we had only been there a week.

Quickly she changed the subject. Why exactly had we come to Tukuyu today, she now wanted to know.

So I told her about our being out of food and eating out of tins. And about the smell in our *choo.* She said she knew just the thing, that they would take us over to the market this afternoon. Somehow I hadn't thought there could be two markets . . . I knew she couldn't mean the one that we had passed this morning.

Then she asked whether we had found a houseboy yet to do our cooking and cleaning. I shook my head. But how will you do your work, your teaching, if you must do all the housework yourself? And I thought of Mr. Mwadunda, saying to us that they all had wives and daughters who did their housework, and of the little girl who came from the village every day. Maybe he was right, maybe he really had meant it. And I thought of my pile of dirty laundry. Just who did I think was going to wash my shirts and shorts and mend my socks?

Then she said that she had just the boy. He had worked for a family that had gone back to England just last month. So he was looking for a job. And before I could say anything, she was calling, Ernest, Ernest, *njoo hapa, upesi,* speaking Swahili with a very British accent as the man with the white uniform and bow tie trotted into the room.

She jabbered sharply at him in Swahili and he trotted out. She explained to me that she had just instructed him to have someone go with a message to the boy. That he lived in Masoko which was only ten miles away and that he would report directly to us at school in the next few days. His name was Mbaliki. And I thought of what a wonderful soldier she would have made.

Then Mike came out. He had already turned on the water for my bath so it was almost ready. I went in and took my clothes off, just letting them drop on the floor as I stepped in. Ah, it was hot, and I let myself sink slowly down, feeling the hot water seeping through me, lying there, floating far away as though I could fall off to sleep. I could smell the food cooking, a roast, what a delicious smell, what a delicious feeling lying here in the hot water. Who would ever have thought you could feel this way about a bath?

When I came out we sat down at the table, and Ernest brought in soup. Then he brought in the roast, with gravy and fluffy white potatoes, as I kept piling pieces of meat on my plate.

Mrs. Stark said it had just occurred to her that perhaps we would care to join them at the club this afternoon.

Good idea, said Mr. Stark.

And the dessert, a kind of custard something or other.

The club wasn't really much, Mrs. Stark said, we really shouldn't expect anything too fancy, as so many of them had left already. In fact, she said, there were only about fifteen or twenty families left. But it was still nice, they still had a tennis competition every Sunday morning. Did we play? We would stop at the market afterward, if we didn't mind.

Then Mr. Stark told us that they had been in Africa since before the war, and that he had been connected with some mining operations in gold and mica. In fact only last year he had sold out his share in the mica company to the government, and shortly he and Mrs. Stark were going back to England. Not later than the end of the year, Mrs. Stark interjected.

He seemed so sad when she said it—not later than the end of the year—and then as an afterthought, Yes, but it's been a good life out here, as though he were sighing back his years of memories with these words. I couldn't help thinking of someone else who had said the same thing, that lady from the tea plantation—what was her name, Mrs. Gibson—that's what she had said too, it had been a good life out here. So wistfully, just before she had asked me if I had really come here to help the Africans.

Shall we go? asked Mrs. Stark briskly standing up. To the car then, but not before she had remembered to give us a jar of disinfectant for the *choo*. What a wonderful woman.

Then we were driving into a pebbled, circular driveway, up to a large white building, which was surrounded by thick trees so that it was difficult to see it very clearly from the outside. Inside was a large barroom which was empty, but there were loud shouts coming from another room. We followed the noise around to another bar where there were about ten or fifteen people—so much noise from so few people. As we entered, they let out a loud whoop, some of them running up to us offering to buy us a drink. I looked around and recognized most of the people from Martin Martinson's. And there was Martin Martinson himself, sitting at the bar, smiling, quite drunk. Have a drink.

It was good to see us, they said to Mike and me, we should come down more often. They were having a smasher of a party this evening, were we coming? And tomorrow, every Sunday, a tennis competition, were we coming to that? And above it you could hear shouts of Boy, boy, Henry, Henry—he was the little gray-haired African who served drinks.

They kept asking us, Are you coming tonight? And they were so hurt when we said we weren't. Why not, they wanted to know. They needed people so badly, it seemed, as though all the noise, all the whoops, were really to make up for the fact that there were only ten or fifteen of them there, that somehow we had come when the party was over, and that they almost knew it themselves.

I wanted to explain to them why not—why we weren't coming— and I thought of trying to tell Mrs. Stark or even Martin Martinson that we had really come here to Africa to be part of the African way of life, to share or adapt or adjust to their customs or whatever it is, as best we could. But I figured they would never understand what I meant. I wasn't even sure whether I understood myself.

Afterward Mrs. Stark drove us down to the marketplace at the bottom of the hill, the same one we had passed this morning, the little old women in their rags still sitting where we had seen them, their food still on the ground in rows. Maybe they would bring it back tomorrow if they could not sell it today.

● Mrs. Stark stopped the car and got out. She had brought a little basket and was walking into the market, right into the middle of those women—there wasn't another market after all—picking up the food on the ground, feeling the onions, mangoes, rice, beans, speaking to them in very rapid, soldierlike Swahili, squeezing an orange here, a tomato there, shaking an egg, putting them all into her basket and dispensing small coins to the old women.

Then she walked to the meat that was drying in the sun and covered with flies. She bought four pounds and they wrapped it for her in an old newspaper and she put it in the basket with the rest. And seeing I was looking at her as if to say, You don't really think I am going to eat that, do you, she said very sternly, There's nothing to be squeamish about. All the food you ate today came right here from this market. Then a little more kindly, Really, there's nothing so dirty about the meat or any of the vegetables once you cook them. And the eggs and fruits all have shells or skins. Really, and she smiled at us, and you could not help smiling back.

· · ·

There was a letter slipped under our door the next day. An invitation! You are cordially requested at the house of Mr. Biboko, the assistant headmaster, for some Sunday pombelization.

Pombelization. A good English word. Derived from pombe. I hadn't realized Mr. Biboko had a sense of humor.

When we arrived at his house, Mr. Biboko was sitting at a table with another teacher, whose name was Mr. Ngubile. There was a large bowl of pombe between them, brown and bubbly. They jumped up as we entered and pulled up two chairs around the table, shaking hands with us very enthusiastically.

We have heard that you are great pombe drinkers, Mr. Biboko said very grandiloquently, that he had heard how we had drunk pombe at Bwana Mbulu's hut late into the night until it was all finished.

How had he heard about that, I wondered. He should only know how it really had been there at Bwana Mbulu's, what with our trying to get up and leave every few seconds.

He went on, as he passed me the bowl, that we would always be welcome at his house. I tried to take a good-sized gulp, but I started coughing instead, and Mr. Biboko and Mr. Ngubile burst into laughter, sticking out their hands and slapping palms, the way we had seen Mr. Twakatulu and Mr. Mwambigila do. Then Mr. Biboko held out his palm for me, and we slapped while I tried my best not to choke on that damned pombe, which seemed to be caught halfway in my throat.

Mr. Ngubile said that they called this pombe local stuff because it was prepared locally, by local women of the villages. We had a big laugh on that—local stuff, another vintage phrase. He said that he was the number one drinker and that Mr. Biboko was number two. There were two others who also drank very much, we would meet them this afternoon. They had a kind of club, he said, they called themselves the life-ists, because they enjoyed life so much. Life-ists. A beautiful word, I thought. These gentlemen certainly had an interesting vocabulary.

Yes, he continued, he was life-ist number 1 and Mr. Biboko was life-ist number 2. We could be three and four if we liked. So we had a laugh and slapped palms to that, passing the bowl around again, and Mr. Biboko said that everyone of the life-ists was a *broo,* which was short for brother, so I would be a broo and Mike would be a broo also, and we slapped palms again as the bowl came back to me.

Mr. Biboko said that Mr. Ngubile was the young *broo* because he was only thirty-one years old while Mr. Biboko was thirty-four. I am the old man, he said, the *babu.* That means grandfather in Swahili. And he smiled, Why don't you call me Babu as it shows great respect?

All right, Babu, I said.

Then Mr. Mwadunda came in and some other teachers whom I recognized but whose names I didn't know. We all shook hands and they seemed very pleased and surprised to see us there as they fitted themselves around the table, sitting two to a chair now since there weren't enough chairs for everyone.

They began speaking to each other in Swahili while we tried to catch what they were saying. Of course we couldn't, but we tried to seem interested anyway, and the bowl kept going around and around as they drank deeply in turn, slapping palms with each other amid great roars of laughter and shouts of *broo, broo.*

A lady came in, wearing a brightly colored dress, barefoot,

carrying a bowl of pombe on her head. Mr. Biboko leaned toward us and whispered, That is my wife.

Yes—I nodded my head, I remembered her. She was the one who had first whipped out her breast at the tea party.

She poured her bowl into the one on the table, more brown and bubbly with a dirtyish white foam. Then she went out to the back yard, leaving the door open.

There in the back through the open door you could see three little children, maybe five or six years old, sitting on the ground, playing in the dirt, wearing torn clothes, barefoot, two girls in ragged, unwashed dresses, and a little boy with only a shirt, nothing for bottoms, like the little children we had passed on the road.

Then a chicken flew into the house through the open door, squawking and running around while the teachers sat there, pretending not to notice, just passing the bowl without a word. Finally the chicken found itself a place in the corner and sat there clucking quietly to itself.

Outside the children had begun fighting with each other. The little boy was crying, and Mr. Biboko called out sharply to him in Swahili. My children, he said to me in a confidential tone as the little boy waddled toward him through the door, half naked. It seemed so strange, Mr. Biboko with his education, his English vocabulary. An intelligent man. And his wife like the wife of any African villager, the little children dressed like urchins, the chicken inside squawking contentedly in the corner, no one making any attempt whatsoever to throw it outside—they didn't even seem to notice it.

The little boy approached him, and seeing me, he suddenly began to shriek, running back toward the door. The teachers burst into a great roar, nodding their heads to each other, saying *Rangi, rangi, shauri ya rangi,* which meant it was because of my skin. That's why he was so afraid. It was kind of funny actually. Never thought *that* would happen to me.

Mr. Biboko said to everyone now that we were the two new *broos,* and we all slapped palms to that. He said that all *broos* should help each other, wasn't that so? And they all nodded their heads.

One of them asked me what I had been doing, climbing the ladder up the side of my house, and when I told them about the bats they wagged their heads. Then as it dawned on them, they burst into guffaws. Yes, the bats, that house is full of bats, in fact they all. had bats in their homes. But it does no good to chase them, they said. They keep coming back, there is nothing anyone can do, and they laughed and slapped palms again.

Then Mr. Mwadunda spoke to Mr. Biboko in Swahili and Mr. Biboko asked us if we had gotten a cook yet.

Not yet, I said, and they all seemed a little surprised and buzzed quickly to each other.

We should have one, they said, it was necessary because what were we going to do when school began, how were we going to do our work? Yes, that is what Mrs. Stark had said and Mr. Mwadunda. Maybe they were right, maybe we should get someone. What was the name of that man Mrs. Stark had sent? Mbaliki? Wasn't he supposed to be coming any day now?

They were talking about school now—were we aware that the boys would be arriving tomorrow and that classes would begin sometime this week? Did we like science? Mr. Biboko asked us. He liked it very much. And quietly, in confidential tones, he began telling Mike and me, as he was seated between us, how someday he, not Mr. Twakatulu, was going to be headmaster of Ndumulu School, and that he would always remember his young *broos*.

I thought to myself, His English is certainly better than Mr. Twakatulu's.

I was supposed to have been appointed headmaster this year instead of Mr. Twakatulu, he continued, but the headmaster last year did not like me. But someday, he said, someday I will be headmaster.

I sat there, not quite sure what to say, so I just smiled at him. He seemed serious enough although he must be a little drunk. Then I asked him, Why didn't the headmaster last year like you?

He stared at me for a long time and said very seriously and confidentially, nodding his head, He feared me because of my intelligence. Yes, that's it, they all fear me, he said, all these people here because I am from another tribe, from the north. And my tribe is more intelligent, more civilized than the Nyakusa tribe. That's why none of them like me.

I was about to laugh, about to stick my palm out and say, *broo, broo,* that was a good one, except that I suddenly realized that Mr.

Biboko was serious, he was not laughing, he was just staring at me waiting for me to say something, and the smile froze right across my mouth.

Then Mrs. Biboko was back with a large bowl of something very white and fluffy—food—and she placed it on the table, and one of the little girls in a torn dress brought in a bowl of meat with gravy. I couldn't help noticing how dirty the little girl's legs were and how hard her bare feet.

They brought us plates but there weren't enough to go around, so some of the teachers shared one between them. Mr. Biboko told us the white food was called ugali, which is the main African food. They would take a hunk of it in their fingers, working it up into a small ball, all of them reaching from the center at the same time. Then they would dip the ball into the bowl with meat and gravy and plop it into their mouths.

We tried the ugali, Mike and I, it was very soft, and with the gravy soaking into it very sweet and tasty. I grinned without realizing it, and seeing me they roared with laughter, thrilled as little children that I had liked it. And we all slapped our food-stained palms with each other, the bowl going round and round, as we washed the ugali down with the pombe.

When we had finished, Mrs. Biboko returned with a bowl of water for us to rinse our fingers, walking around the table, holding it for each of us in turn. Then all that remained was the bowl of pombe, it went round and round, I began wondering when it would all be over and when we could go home.

Suddenly Mr. Ngubile stopped and said that they should tell the new *broos* the motto of the life-ists. The others all nodded their heads and giggled to each other.

Mr. Ngubile said, The motto is . . . and he stopped, looking around at the others. They were still nodding, looking at him intently as if to say, Yes, yes, go ahead, *broo*.

He started again, The motto is—to steal and cheat the schoolboys. And with that a great roar went up, the chicken started squawking and running and flapping around again. To steal and cheat the schoolboys—it was sort of funny if you looked at it that way. And I thought how nice it was that they felt they could say this in front of us as though they had really and truly accepted us into their circle. As though we were one of them, and so quickly too. Did it matter if what Mr. Ngubile was saying was a lot of rubbish?

• • •

The boys began filtering in the next day. They would come walking through the brick arch in twos and threes, big ones who looked over twenty years old and little ones who seemed not even ten, each of them in short pants and a white shirt, barefoot, carrying on his head a wooden box or a basket with all the belongings he owned in the world.

That afternoon Mr. Biboko came to our house and announced that Mr. Twakatulu wanted to have a meeting with the staff. He led us into a room near the brick arch with the word OFFICE above the door. All the teachers were already inside, sitting crowded together two to a chair as the room was very small, with Mr. Twakatulu standing at the front of the room. Mr. Biboko went and sat next to him, as he was the assistant headmaster, while we squeezed ourselves in with the others.

Mr. Twakatulu smiled nervously to us as we sat down. Then he nodded to Mr. Mwaisunga, who was our neighbor on the other side, and he stood up and began reading the minutes of the last meeting from a large notebook which he held up in front of him like a herald reading a royal proclamation.

The meeting had been held just before we had arrived at Ndumulu. It was all about the preparations for the party—how much each of them was to contribute, how many pounds of sugar and tea, how many loaves of bread and how much jam they were going to buy. And I realized for the first time just how hard they had worked on that tea party, planning every small detail—who would collect the money, who would go to Tukuyu to buy the bread and jam, who would arrange the classroom. And we had run right off to Martin Martinson's that first night, leaving them just standing there after all their preparations, not even realizing.

Mr. Mwaisunga sat down and Mr. Twakatulu motioned to Mr. Mwambigila, who was sitting near the door. He stepped outside and a gnarled old man in a white sheet entered, *Oogonile, oogonile, ndaga, ndaga,* said the teachers and the old man, as Mr. Mwambigila brought in a chair for him.

Mr. Twakatulu said that the old man had something very important to say to all of us. Something about each teacher's having been allotted a certain number of trees to cut down, but that they had been cutting down other trees that weren't theirs.

The old man began speaking—not Swahili but Nyakusa, I could tell because Nyakusa seemed to have a kind of lilt to it, a rise and fall in the tone that Swahili doesn't have. Not that I could understand any of it—*oogonile* and *ngada* was the extent of my Nyakusa.

So we just had to sit there, Mike and I, doing our best to seem interested, as he went on and on. Soon I began squirming in my seat—why didn't he stop?—while the teachers all sat there without a sound, their eyes fixed on him. I looked helplessly over at Mike, whose eyes were just beginning to close.

Finally though, he did stop. I glanced down at my watch. Thirty minutes he had been talking. But now the teachers all had their hands up, they were asking him questions, and the old man would go into very long, deliberate explanations, waving his hands and nodding his head to make his point.

I laughed to myself, it was truly unbelievable, sitting here listening to a thirty minute speech in a strange language. And then waiting while they went through these questions. What could he have said to stimulate such response?

Then it was over, the old man walking around to each of us, touching hands and saying *Oogonege,* which is what a person says when he is leaving. And the teachers answering *Ookagone,* which is what you say to the person who is leaving, as he shuffled out the door.

Then Mr. Twakatulu passed out a paper to each of us. At the top it said Ministry of Education and under that were listed a teacher's duties and responsibilities. There were about twenty items. 1) A teacher is thoughtful, kind and diligent. 2) A teacher should always be well-dressed and present a favorable appearance —something like the Boy Scout manual—all the way down to 17) A teacher should try to help the students at all times. I couldn't help thinking of the life-ist motto, a teacher should steal and cheat the schoolboys.

Mr. Twakatulu said that he would read it aloud while we read it to ourselves. He began at the top of the page reading out the words, Ministry of Education, Duties and Responsibilities of a Teacher, pronouncing every word slowly and deliberately. 1) A teacher is thoughtful, kind and diligent . . . all the way down to 17, as we read it silently, like a third-grade class listening to another third grader and his reading lesson.

When he had finished he asked if there were any questions. None this time. Good for them.

Then he said he was going to read each teacher's schedule and extracurricular activities, which he and Mr. Biboko had drawn up during the week. Mr. Biboko had handed him a sheet of paper and he began.

Mr. Ngubile was teaching English and history to class 8A, Swahili to classes 6A and 6B, and math to class 5A. Mr. Mwadunda math to 6A and 6B, Swahili to 7A and 7B, and geography to 5A and 5B. I was teaching English, math and science to 7A and science to 6A. Mike the same for 7B and 6B. And we were both teaching physical education to Standard 8. Mr. Twakatulu said he wanted us to teach them some American sports.

Sports, I thought. Basketball, baseball. They'd love hitting the ball, I'd bet.

Then Mr. Twakatulu began reading off the list of my extracurricular activities.

Master of sports and outdoor games. More sports. Good. We would really have a chance to work with them. The double play, bunting, sliding—we could teach them all that. Maybe we could even build a basketball court. And show them about a lay-up, a jump shot, a zone defense. I bet some of these kids would be damn good.

Mr. Twakatulu continued reading. English master:

Class master 7A—whatever that meant
Assistant Director of Boys Library
Photography Club
Choral Director

Oops. What was this about photography club and choral director? I didn't know anything about cameras, and I couldn't even carry a tune. How could I possibly teach these things?

Mr. Twakatulu continued reading. Mike's were:

Class master 7B
Master Geographical and Historical Society

Master of Indoor Games and Sports
Assistant Master of Staff Library
Director Science Club
Choral Assistant to the Director
Physical Fitness Committee
Master of Health

My God, I thought. How could we handle all these activities? How would we have the time? There seemed no question now that we must have a cook. Where was that Mbaliki that Mrs. Stark had said was coming?

Then Mr. Twakatulu finished reading, saying he would type a list of the schedule and extracurricular activities and put it on the bulletin board for everyone to see. But some of the teachers objected to this, they didn't think it was proper for the boys to know what went on in staff meetings. And of course they would, they said, if we put the list on the bulletin board.

Mmm, they said, as Mr. Twakatulu nodded his head and waggled his black mustache.

Mmm, Mr. Biboko repeated.

Someone raised his hand. Then the whole room was filled with raised hands. And soon a full-fledged debate had begun. Should we or should we not have the teachers' schedules and extracurricular activities put on the bulletin board? They all wanted to speak, they were straining in their chairs, their arms outstretched, as Mr. Twakatulu went around the room calling on each of them in turn. My God, how stupid. What difference could it possibly make? And when Mr. Twakatulu called on me, that was just what I wanted to say.

But I didn't, of course. I said that this was a decision for the headmaster himself to decide, and Mr. Twakatulu nodded his head. Yes, he thought so too. He would decide himself. The meeting was adjourned, and he stood up.

Was it really over? Finally? I looked at my watch. We had been in there for nearly three hours. It was incredible, the whole thing shouldn't have taken any longer than thirty minutes, if that. And what was I going to do about the choral group or the photography club?

When we reached our house there was a man waiting to see us.

46

Very thin, with a long, black mustache, wearing trousers and a sport shirt and shined shoes. He said his name. Mbaliki. He had come.

We began talking, and he said in English that he didn't know any English, and he pried out a notebook from his back pocket. I noticed that he was wearing a ring with a great blue stone on his middle finger. But it was a woman's ring, the kind you can buy at Woolworth's. Maybe it had been given to him as a present, perhaps by this last European he had just been working for. Maybe he was wearing it to impress us.

He handed me the notebook. It contained references written by various employers. Actually I couldn't read their handwritings very well, but he insisted that I look carefully at the little book, so I screwed up my face, nodding my head and saying, Mmm, very sternly, and handed it to Mike who did the same. Mm, Mmmm.

So we agreed on a price, 105 shillings—about fifteen dollars a month—which they had told us was about average. For that he said he would cook, clean, wash and iron, do all the things we needed done. A bona fide houseboy, all right. Only he said he would first have to go back to Masoko to get his family—he had a wife and two babies—and bring them to Ushirika, where they would live.

Ushirika. Those tiny mud huts. How could a whole family live in one of those?

But that was his problem, and I tried not to think about it. I had enough of my own. Master of the Photography Club and Choral Director.

•    •    •

Classes began the next day. But first there was an assembly, with the whole school lined up in rows of white shirts and white shorts, as the band played the national anthem. There were about fifty pupils in the band, a third of them girls—somehow I hadn't realized that the school was coed. They stood out in front of the others in three long rows, banging drums and whistling flutelike things that made a high, shrill noise, the girls each carrying a small green box filled with stones, which they jiggled in time to the music.

Then the band started to play something that sounded strangely enough, like "Believe Me If All Those Endearing Young Charms," as the teachers went toward the rows of schoolboys. Mr. Biboko whispered to me that it was the class master's duty to inspect his class as he led me to 7A. I watched how the other teachers were inspecting, walking up and down the rows of white shirts, pulling at their hair, tugging at their uniforms, to see that they were clean maybe, or perhaps that their buttons were buttoned.

After we had finished inspecting, the band played a march and the pupils marched off to their classrooms, black arms swinging, a sea of white shirts, with Mr. Twakatulu screaming at the top of his lungs, Eyes front, eyes front.

I went to class for the first time and the boys all stood stiffly at attention as I walked in the door.

Good morning, class, I said.

Good morning, sir, they said in chorus.

Be seated, I said. The only sound now the scraping of chairs along the floor as they fitted themselves under their desks.

They sat there in white shirts and white shorts, their bare feet sticking out from under their desks, looking up at me with big black eyes, more than forty of them in that tiny classroom. Some of them were big boys, who looked older than I. Others were so small that they couldn't have been more than ten or eleven years old.

I began telling them something about myself and where I came from, America. There was not a sound in the room. I could feel their big eyes on me, but no noise, nothing, and I wondered if they could understand. Then I said how happy I was to be here in Tanganyika, and especially at Ndumulu School, the way Mike had at the tea party, and they smiled, showing big white teeth. They could understand. Then someone coughed, and I noticed a little boy in the doorway. How long had he been standing there, I wondered.

He handed me a note. There was a staff meeting now in the office, and I was to go there immediately. I wondered what it could be, it must be very important to stop classes. So I said, Good morning, boys, and they stood up and said, Good morning, sir, as I walked out the door.

They were all in their seats waiting for me, with Mr. Twakatulu and Mr. Biboko in the front of the room. As I sat down, Mr. Mwaisunga stood up and began reading the minutes of yesterday's meeting, and I had to hear about the old man and the trees and listen to those ridiculous arguments again about should we or should we not have the schedule placed on the bulletin board.

Then Mr. Twakatulu read us a letter he had received that day, that Mr. Kitandalala, the school inspector, was coming to Ndumulu at the end of the week. I thought it seemed like a strange time to inspect, during the first week of the year.

Mr. Twakatulu said that it meant that the school must be ready for him, that the grounds must all be cleaned, the grass cut, and he invited suggestions as to what we should do. We talked it over for a while and Mr. Ngubile said that instead of holding afternoon classes this week, the boys should work from two to five o'clock cleaning the school.

They all seemed to like that idea, so we voted on it, and Mr. Twakatulu sent Mr. Mwambigila to go and call a boy to ring the alarm bell. In a few seconds we heard it, *gong, gong, gong,* sharp and rapid as the boys all came pouring out of their classes, running to the assembly ground, a horde of white shirts and shorts, black arms and legs.

Mr. Twakatulu led the teachers out there, and we set about organizing them into groups, as Mr. Twakatulu appointed a leader or prefect for each. He spoke to them in Swahili, explaining what he wanted them to do, I guess, and they marched off in their groups, while we returned to the office. There was another order of business, Mr. Twakatulu said—it was to decide the prefects for the year.

Prefects, Mr. Biboko said to us, were the leaders of the boys, to be chosen from among the boys to supervise the others.

Mr. Twakatulu read off a list of the prefects—dormitory prefects, library prefects, dining hall prefects, health prefects, day, night, girl prefects, just about every kind of prefect you could think of. Then he read a list of the ninety boys in Standard 8. As they were the oldest boys, the prefects should be chosen from them.

Then as Mr. Twakatulu began reading off the names of the boys in Standard 8, the teachers said yes or no. If there weren't too many no's, Mr. Mwaisunga would write down the boy's name, so that from the ninety boys in Standard 8, Mr. Mwaisunga had written down fifty of them after the first go-round. As there were thirty prefects in the school, it was just a question of eliminating twenty of these.

But Mr. Twakatulu said that we must be sure, as this was a very important decision we were making. That we should go into one of the classrooms where there was a blackboard so that we could see all the names in front of us so we could decide more carefully.

So we got up and moved into the 5A classroom, which was just next door. As we walked outside, we could see the boys, the entire school, working on the grounds in their groups, some with hoes, some with wheelbarrows, some with *pangas* cutting the grass. Others with brooms—really bunches of thick leaves from trees— sweeping the paths, the girls pruning the flowers, with the prefects of each group standing nearby, helping and overseeing. And they were all working, and working hard, without any grumbling or complaining, each doing his assigned job—like an army of ants, like no schoolchildren I had ever seen before.

I said to Mr. Biboko that I was impressed with the way these students were working. He looked at me and said, Don't they work this way in America? I thought of how I had been, how I was as a schoolboy, always trying to get out of work, and I said, Well, at least not from two o'clock to five.

They must do as we tell them here, he said. We are their teachers. We are like fathers to them and they must obey. Did I know that there were 360 boys here and that each teacher was like the president of all 360 of them? Yes, he said, they must do whatever we tell them.

Then we were in the classroom, Mr. Mwaisunga writing all fifty names on the board. Now the arguments began, each name taking a little longer to discuss. For each teacher seemed to have one or two special boys that he wanted, so he would talk against all the other boys to make sure that his boy was picked. They would say things like Yes, he is a good student, but he is too small, the boys would not fear him, or Yes, he is very big and strong, but he is very bad in the classroom. Or that his English was not good enough—what would happen if a guest came to the school? So at the end of round two, nearly two hours later, there were only three boys left whom they all agreed upon.

Finally Mr. Twakatulu said that perhaps if he chose the boys himself tonight, we could discuss it tomorrow and the next day. It might be easier that way. And they all agreed, yes it would be easier, a much better idea.

So every afternoon that week we had a staff meeting to discuss Mr. Twakatulu's choices for prefects. And every afternoon from two to five the boys worked on the grounds.

And Mr. Kitandalala, the school inspector, never came.

They had given us physical education to teach to the Standard 8's. They were big boys, the 8's, some of them older than we were, and we'd see them swaggering and smirking around the school, the way all boys do, I guess, when they are the biggest and the oldest.

We decided to give them a real workout for P.E., Mike and I, to see if they would still be swaggering and smirking when we finished with them. So as they sauntered out of their class down to the field for the first time, we suddenly ran at them, each of us carrying a little stick, shouting at them to hurry up, that they were at P.E. now, and that they could warm up by running once around the outside of the field.

They loped off, laughing to each other, Warm up, warm up, their white teeth gleaming.

They were still laughing as they finished running, and we herded them into a circle. Mike ran into the center and showed them how he wanted them to do jumping jacks, counting out loud, One—two —three—four, jumping with their feet spread apart, their arms clapping over their heads on the count of one, their legs together, their arms down at their sides on two.

They began, a bit timorously, and we snarled at them, Scream out those numbers, as they jumped. One—two—three—four. They liked this, they thought it was great fun, as they roared One—two —three—four, the thump of their feet on the ground as they landed.

All right, Mike said, and suddenly I raced into the center of the circle, knees churning high, yelling at them, Get those knees up, get 'em up. They laughed, running in place now, their knees shooting into the air as I screamed at them, Higher, higher.

All right, I said, flipping my stick to Mike. They stopped.

Now, arms out straight. Stiff. Shoulder height.

Keep them out. Straight. No slackers. No talking.

The boys stood there with their arms outstretched now. Without a sound.

One minute. They were looking at each other questioningly now, as if they didn't quite know what to make of this.

Two minutes. I had to put my arms down because it hurt, and I walked around them menacingly.

They were grimacing now. But not a sound from them. Maybe they were afraid.

Swing them now, I called to them, and I moved my arms in a little circle. Keep them stiff.

You could feel the pain on their faces. But still no noise. You had to give these kids credit.

Three minutes. All right, arms down.

A great sigh swept through them as they began smiling to each other. They thought they were finished.

Start running, Mike shouted at them as he flipped me back my stick.

One lap, I shouted as we began chasing them around the field. Like a herd of animals.

No slackers, I yelled, keep it up.

One of them tried to cut a corner, but Mike grabbed him and flicked him ón the rear with his stick. He squealed like a little pig as the rest of them roared with laughter, thundering past me, ninety of them, their footsteps *clump, clump* like horses. Speed up, speed up, I screamed, and we corralled them back into a circle again.

Down on your backs, Mike roared, and they did it now without a sound.

Now, lift your feet six inches off the ground. Stiff. Only six inches, no more. Stiff, don't bend them.

Keep them there. Hold it.

They did, without a word.

All right. Down.

A thunder of *clumps* as their feet hit the ground. A sigh went through them. But not for long.

Up again, Mike cried. They raised them up again.

Hold them there. Hold it. Now count to ten. One, two, three . . .

Down. *Clump*. Their feet hitting the ground.

Up again. Hold it. Now spread them apart—still stiff. You could hear a gasp from them as they did it, but still no grumbling from them.

Hold them there. Still stiff, only six inches. Back together again. A faint ripple.

Hold them there. Still up. Still stiff.

And down.

*Clump*.

Up again. Hold it. Stiff. Still stiff.

And down. And with that Mike rolled over into a pushup position, leaning on his hands, as I ordered the boys to roll over like

Mike, still in their circle, as Mike bent down to the ground and then up, a pushup, showing them what he wanted them to do.

Now, he called to them. Down, bending with them as he said it. They bent down, their chests nearly touching the ground.

Up. Back to the leaning position.

Down.

Up.

Down.

Up.

Faster now. Down, up. Down, up.

And there was not a sound from them. Not a peep. They did just what they were told. Down, up. Down, up. No more laughter in their eyes.

Down again. Now hold it, Mike called to them.

Say it, I shrieked to them. Say it. Say, Hold it. Like this, Ho-o-old it.

Ho-o-o-old it, Mike called out to them again. Come on. Say it.

And they said it, they roared it out, all of them, *Ho-o-o-old it*. They roared it from the bottom of their guts. All the groans and sighs that we had forced from them through these exercises—all came out with a mighty HO-O-O-OLD IT.

Ho-o-o-old it, Mike called to them again.

And they roared back, HO-O-O-OLD IT. It seemed to reverberate across the whole field. You could see black heads popping out of classroom windows, staring down toward us on the field, at the boys all in a circle down in pushup position, bellowing at the top of their lungs, HO-O-O-OLD IT.

Down, And Mike called out, Si-i-imba, which means lion in Swahili.

And they hollered back, SI-I-IMBA. The smiles had come back to the boys. You could hear the smiles as they let themselves go.

Mike again. Si-i-imba.

And the boys. SI-I-IMBA.

All right, I yelled. And I ran at them with my stick. Everybody up and running. Another lap. One lap, one lap. No slackers.

They ran. Into a sprint this time. Smiling now, laughing and calling out to each other, showing their great white teeth, sprinting now, faster than before, feeling the way you do when you have been challenged and you have come out all right. Better than all right.

The P.E. with the Standard 8's became the high point of their day. They would trot out briskly and race around the track into positions in the circle, and we would send them through their paces, yelling out our instructions to them at the top of our lungs, One—two—three—four, or Get 'em up, NO slackers. If one of them was dawdling or lagging, I would run at him shaking my stick in his face and screaming, You, you, you, while they would all roar in delight. And when they got to the HO-O-O-OLD IT and the SI-I-IMBA, they would shake the field with their voices, and the heads would start popping out of the classrooms.

A group of old women who came each day to sell bananas by the edge of the field—seeing the boys doing their exercises or me hollering at them, You, you, you, or Mike chasing them around the field or flicking someone's rear if he cut a corner—would goggle and oo-oo-ooh and clap their hands and shriek in their high-pitched shrill whistle. Even the teachers started coming to see the boys at their P.E. Not just to see the boys, of course, us too, the way we ran around the field chasing them and screaming at the top of our lungs. And after each performance, Mr. Twakatulu would rush out to us, saying, Thank you, thank you, very, very, bubbling about how much they enjoyed it all, how the villagers were always coming to see us, and that one day we would have to do it in Tukuyu, in front of the whole town, that's how wonderful it was.

Very, very.

Some weeks later, Mr. Twakatulu called a staff meeting to announce that he had received a letter saying that there was to be a political rally in Tukuyu next Saturday. All the schools were to compete in a marching competition, with the winning school receiving a new set of drums. We talked it over—taking nearly the whole morning—and finally we decided that the whole school should practice marching every afternoon that week instead of going to classes.(What better way was there to practice marching than to march?) And that we teachers would hire a taxi Saturday morning to take us to Tukuyu—it would only cost one shilling each if we all shared the cab. Of course the boys would walk, they said, as it was only seven miles. Besides they were very strong.

So the boys marched every afternoon that week, the band squeaking "Believe Me If All Those Endearing Young Charms," the black arms swinging, the white shirts marching down and back, up and around the field, the teachers yelling, Eyes front, eyes front. From two to five in the afternoon, five days a week. Eyes front, eyes front.

On Saturday we twelve teachers crowded into a taxi, sitting on laps, between legs, on top of other laps, with the drums of the band tied to the roof. The boys had left two hours earlier and were to wait for us just outside Tukuyu at the Catholic mission.

There they were as we pulled up, and we readied them into their lines, outfitting the band with the drums. Now we began marching into the center of town, the drums pounding, the flutes piping, the girls bouncing the stones in the boxes, the white shorts and white shirts swinging their black arms, looking straight ahead. Eyes front, eyes front. Marching along in lines of four, 360 of them, the largest school in the region, while we teachers walked alongside, meeting other schools, each with its band also, the same drums, the same flutes, the same squeaky noises.

Now the whole street was filled with noises, each band playing its own songs, drums pounding, flutes tooting, arms pumping, people bumping, black faces, white uniforms, each school marching with its band first, then its little boys with their big eyes, back to their tallest student. And from the opposite direction another line of schools . . . going in both directions now on the street, people bumping together and squeezing past, a mass of white shirts and white shorts.

Men were standing along the sides in faded black tuxedo coats, women in bright long dresses, the reds, oranges and yellows, and some with bright red or green sandals. And Mike and I walked along with the teachers, feeling the crowd's glances on our back— our white backs.

The teachers were busy shaking hands with other teachers from other schools and people on the sidelines, *Oogonile, ndaga, ndaga, oogonile.* They were pulling us with them, introducing us, the two new *broos*, as we would jabber our *Oogonile, ndaga,* and they would all burst into smiles at hearing us speaking Kinyakusa.

Gradually we began drifting toward the center of town, to a large open field just opposite the marketplace. In the center was a large platform with several men sitting in long tribal robes that flowed down over their knees. The schoolboys still in their lines formed a semicircle around them, their bands still pounding and squeaking as they marched in place, the rest of us standing around the outside.

The men on the platform stood up and began walking through the myriad lines of schoolboys as though to inspect them, swinging their shoulders, almost swaggering, hard, severe scowls on their faces. They would walk up one line and down another, their robes trailing behind them on the ground, looking thoroughly unpleasant, almost bored by the whole proceedings. I wondered if they were wearing underwear under those robes.

They walked back up to the platform now and sat down. Then one of them stood up and raised his arms over his head. Suddenly the noise of the bands stopped and a great silence draped itself across the field.

The man began to speak, lifting his arms again and shouting, *Uhuru.*

And the crowd roared back, raising their hands over their heads, *Uhuru.*

He said it again, only louder. *Uhuruuuu.* And the crowd answered, *Uhuruuuu.*

Then he started speaking in Swahili, raising his arms and shouting out his words, *Yajenga nchi, yajenga nchi.* I asked Mr. Ngubile what it was all about and he said, Don't worry, *broo,* it's not important, just something about building the country.

When the man finished the one next to him stood up, raising his arms over his head and shouting, *Uhuru.* And the crowd roared back, *Uhuru.*

Then he cried out, *Uhuru na TANU*—TANU is the national political party of Tanganyika—and the crowd screamed back, *Uhuru na TANU.* He began speaking to them, only he would stop every few seconds and scream, *Uhuru na TANU,* and they would all roar it back in unison, *Uhuru na TANU.*

I glanced across the crowd as they stood there listening and screaming, those men in the tuxedo coats, the women in the bright dresses, most of them barefoot, the half-naked children and the little old men in rags—all of them howling out these words, *Uhuru, uhuru na TANU,* as though this were wonderful entertainment for them, hearing a speech and screaming together with the speaker.

The next one got up and went through the same ritual, and the next and the next. Then I saw someone walking up onto the platform. It was the Twak, Mr. Twakatulu, and he was whispering something in the speaker's ear. The speaker announced something to the crowd, and all the schoolboys started moving back toward the sidelines, blending in with the rest of the crowd. But some boys remained in the center of the field, boys from Ndumulu, the Standard 8 boys. And Mr. Biboko was running over to us, Mike and me, saying that we were supposed to do our P.E. exercises now, that's what the speaker had just announced.

And suddenly I got this feeling in my stomach—the same feeling that I had gotten when Bwana Mbulu had placed the pombe under my nose and said Drink. I looked at Mike. He was looking at me with a horrible expression that I knew I must have also.

Then it seems to come to us at the same time—out of fear, no doubt—we begin charging out on the field, with me shrieking at the top of my lungs, Get 'em up, get those knees up, no slackers. And the boys seeing us tearing out there, break into great smiles, kicking their knees, running in place, their white teeth gleaming as we chase them into a circle.

Mike runs into the center and starts the jumping jacks. One, two, three, four, and the boys roar it back, One, two, three, four, sharp staccato, as we have taught them.

And the crowd roars—they love this noise— as I order them into pushup position.

Down. And we are down touching our chests on the ground.

Up. Back in the leaning position.

Down.

Up.

Faster. Down, up.

Down, up.

Down. And I call out to the boys, Ho-o-o-old it.

They call back, HO-O-O-OLD IT. And a flutter of applause floats out of the crowd.

Si-i-imba, I call.

And the boys, SI-I-IMBA, as a great roar bursts from the crowd. Again. Si-i-imba.

And the boys, screaming now as loud as they can, SI-I-IMBA. The crowd roaring.

Then from where he is standing, Mike cries *Uhuru.*

And the boys answer, still in their pushup positions, *Uhuru.* As the crowds howls.

57

Now Mike again, *Uhuru na TANU*.

And the boys, *Uhuru na TANU*. And the crowd screams.

And now me yelling, *Uhuru na Ndumulu*, the boys *Uhuru na Ndumulu*, as the crowd roars again.

We begin walking off the field to that last roar—that's enough for one day—as Mr. Twakatulu rushes out to us through the crowd, breathless, Thank you, thank you, very, very, as though he might have a heart attack any minute. And there are a swarm of people crowding around us now, all trying to pump our hands, now the men in their robes walking off the platform and coming up to us, no scowls now, they are beaming, they want to shake hands, as we say *Oogonile, ndaga* to them, and they answer *Asante sana, asante sana,* thank you very much. Then they start speaking English, realizing perhaps that we don't understand Swahili: How is Ndumulu?

Mr. Twakatulu had the taxi ready to take us back to school. The other teachers were all inside as we landed gently on top of them, the drums already tied to the roof. The Twak was in ecstasy. He kept saying, Ah, ahh, as though he were going to faint, and over and over, They liked it very much, they liked it very much.

Mr. Biboko and Mr. Ngubile got out at Ushirika. Did we want to come with them?

All right.

So we got out with them while the taxi went on to Ndumulu, and followed them over across the main road down a little path which cut down a valley and up again the other side. To a clearing that was surrounded by tall trees, with groups of old men sitting on the ground, drinking pombe.

We sat down, Mr. Biboko, Mr. Ngubile, Mike and I, as an old woman came and brought us a bowl of pombe. The old men began coming over to us, *Oogonile, ndaga*, sitting down and drinking from our bowl.

Then another group of old men, some with turbans wrapped around their heads like Bwana Mbulu's, sat down. They started speaking to Mr. Ngubile and Mr. Biboko in Kinyakusa, and Mr. Biboko told us that they were thanking us for having come to Tanganyika to help them. Some of them had been in Tukuyu, he said, and they had enjoyed it very much.

Then one old man started speaking very rapidly, nodding his head and becoming very excited, as they all nodded their heads to his words. Mr. Biboko explained that the old man was saying how happy he was to see us here drinking together with all of them. Because he had seen the British before who would never mix with them, who would never speak to them, and he had thought that all white men were like that. Now seeing us here, he knew it was not true.

Suddenly he stopped speaking and smiled at us, this old man. It seemed to make him so happy just seeing us here enjoying ourselves with them, sitting there together on the ground drinking from the bowl. I looked around me at the others, and they were also smiling, these old men without any teeth, they looked almost like babies in a way with their bare gums. They seemed so friendly, so pleased to have us sitting there with them, so happy it was enough to make me happy.

·     ·     ·

It wasn't long before the days began to take on a kind of routine, they seemed to flow into each other, one day into the next, each one just like the one before it and the one after it, and before you knew it, it was a week, and then another week. I would wake up around 6:30, usually to a rooster crowing outside my window—or if not that, then it would be Mr. Mwadunda's children screaming to each other as they ran past my house. And Mbaliki would be puttering softly around the kitchen, preparing our breakfast.

Actually Mbaliki was working out very well. He had moved his family from Masoko to Ushirika, and now they lived in one of those mud huts along the side of the road—four of them in one hut, one room, where they cooked and ate and slept and God knows what else. He was very efficient, always on time in the morning for making breakfast, and in the evening for preparing dinner—he was free after lunch except that he had to come back to cook supper— very obedient, always doing whatever we told him without a murmur, like doing the washing today and the ironing tomorrow, or scrubbing the floor or sweeping under the bed—all without a complaint, just *Ndiyo, bwana, ndiyo, bwana,* Yes, sir.

Now, faintly, I could hear the flick of the match as he lit the kerosene stove and started pumping to build up the pressure; the sound of eggs being beaten in a bowl—we usually had eggs and toast and tea and oranges for breakfast. We could even buy packets of butter in Tukuyu, we had discovered.

After breakfast they would begin bonging the bell, and the boys would run to the assembly ground in their whites, the big ones loping on their long legs, the little ones trotting on their short legs, the band playing the national anthem, and those boys who weren't yet in line, stopping and standing still at attention.

I would be coming from my house as all the teachers would be ambling up, shaking hands with everyone, smiling, laughing— Good morning, Broo, how are you? How did you sleep last night? How have you been since yesterday?— as though we were a tribe of long-lost brothers, seeing each other for the first time in thirty years.

Then the band would break into "Believe Me If All Those Endearing Young Charms," as we would sally forth to the lines to inspect our classes, the boys standing stiffly at attention in their whites. Somehow I never did find out exactly what it was we were supposed to inspect, so I would just walk up and down, giving each of them a very cold, hard stare, the way I had seen the speakers in Tukuyu do, or maybe pull at some boy's hair if it was especially dirty or tug at someone's uniform if it had too many buttons missing—purely to keep everybody happy.

Classes were supposed to begin at eight, but usually just as the school began marching to classrooms, the Twak would come bouncing out of the office, shooing the boys back into their lines. He would begin haranguing them, first reminding the Standard 8's that they had their exam this year and that they weren't studying hard enough, or perhaps some boy was late, or his uniform wasn't clean, or the prefect had reported that he hadn't done his work the day before.

The Twak would call out all those names, and each boy would walk timidly up to the front and lie down on the ground in pushup position while the teacher on duty for the week would come toward him with his stick, the whole school pushing closer to get a better look. The stick would come down, hard, whistling strokes—they weren't fooling—the boy cringing and wriggling on the ground. One, two, three, four! Or if it was more serious, a theft, if some boy had gone off for a day or so without permission—they seemed to do that periodically, these boys—then Mr. Ngubile would do the beating—they called him the commander because he beat so hard —with the Twak yelling and cursing at the boy between strokes, You bloody changuku—whatever a changuku was—or you Shenzi bastard. Three, four, five, six—by now the boy might begin to cry and plead—seven, eight, and the Twak would send him off with a final kick on his rear to the gleeful howls of the onlookers.

Mike and I asked the Twak about it one day—maybe there was another way to punish the boys instead of beating them. But he shook his head vehemently—muttering something about the stick being the only thing they understood.

But maybe we could try another way, an experiment perhaps. But he said No, peremptorily.

Finally the band would play again, and the school would march off to the classrooms. I would go to 7A and struggle through the attendance register of their Swahili names, every name that I pronounced incorrectly sending the boys into fits of laughter, while I stood there and smiled wryly—what else can you do?

Into math and then English, and I would go to 6A for science and then P.E. with the 8's and that would take us up to twelve o'clock, when we broke for lunch—unless there was a staff meeting, which could begin at any time, and we would leave the boys sitting there to work on their own.

And—in a word—these kids were bright. But more than just bright, they were eager. They would sit there at attention, staring at me with their big eyes, without making a sound. And at first I would think it was that they didn't understand me or that they weren't paying attention, but every time I would say a new word or write something on the board, I would see them taking out their notebooks and scribbling in them without ever saying a word.

And after a while they began to ask questions, What was that I had said, sir, or Would I please write that word on the board, sir. Could you use it in a sentence, sir?

No, they weren't afraid to speak up, these kids, and they would ask good sensible questions about the lesson we had just had. Like about quadrilaterals, where I told them that a square, a rectangle, a parallelogram, were all special kinds of quadrilaterals. And one of them asked, But then isn't a square also a special kind of rectangle? and I'd say, Yes, that's exactly right, why is it special? And they'd say right off, Because the sides are all equal. And then someone else would have his hand up, What about a parallelogram, then, what would you call that if its sides were equal, wouldn't that also be a special kind of parallelogram?

Yes, questions like that—good questions—which made me know

that they had really understood. And the bell might ring and I would begin to walk out the door, but some hands would still be up so I'd take another question or two, and that would only cause more hands to go up.

And some who hadn't gotten it in class would begin stopping by my house. Could I explain to them just once more about the square and the rectangle? Or could I correct an extra composition that they had done, or some extra sums?

At night you could walk by the classrooms and see them studying, forty of them, bent over their desks, scribbling by the shadowy light of a pressure lamp hanging from the ceiling. And the Standard 8's would study until late into the night, as their exam for secondary school was at the end of the year—except that only one-third of them would pass as they didn't have enough places for them all, since there were so few secondary schools and even fewer teachers. And if they failed their exam, what could they do, as there were no jobs for them? Only go back to their villages.

But bright and eager as they were, these boys, they just didn't know anything. Not that they were stupid or dull or that they couldn't learn, no, nothing like that—just look how quickly they had picked up the math. And in fact their English was not so bad at all, certainly good enough to understand what I was saying most of the time, and remember they had begun to speak English in grade four, which was only three years ago.

No, it was nothing like that, it was just—well, in math they were so slow, they would spend ten minutes doing one long-division problem, and they could never finish even the easiest of tests on time. And I began to discover that many of these boys—and this was grade seven—could not do fundamentals like fractions or multiply correctly, or would add eight and five and get fourteen.

But more than that—it wasn't merely math—they just didn't seem to have any conception of things. Take science, for example. I brought them to the house once to demonstrate that water has more than one form, showing them the fridge, taking out a tray of ice, telling them to touch the ice cubes. Warily, they stuck out their fingers . . . and jumped back with squeals. Standing there, licking their fingers, stupefied—how could anything be so cold?—with no idea at all what it was they had touched. And then, as the ice in the tray melted . . . the disbelief in their faces as they watched it trickle into water. Pouring it into a glass now and letting them take a sip. They were looking at each other, laughing and smiling—those great white teeth—it really was water . . . all the while casting furtive, sidelong glances at me as though they weren't completely sure it hadn't all been some kind of trick.

Or when I happened to show them a picture one day, something I had cut out of some magazine, of two sailors standing on the bridge of a ship in a harbor, the sun shining on the water, the skyline of New York in the background. They had no idea what it was all about. Not the skyline—of course, they couldn't be expected to know what skyscrapers look like—but they didn't even know these men were on a ship. They didn't know that it was a ship, they didn't notice that these were uniforms that the men were wearing. They just stared blankly, shaking their heads.

And how easy it would be to say, Well, they just don't know anything, they must be stupid or dull. But no, that wasn't it at all. It was just that when you got hold of these boys—even here in Standard 7—you were practically dealing with a clean slate. A real *tabula rasa*. As if they knew literally nothing about anything. And in English it wasn't hard, they had textbooks for that, and I would give them exercises to do each night and one or two compositions a week, since they were so enthusiastic. And in math about twenty sums a night, because they just needed drill and more drill.

But it was this other field, science and general knowledge, that was so hard. First, there was only one book—for the teacher—which described how to do experiments, and some of them you couldn't do because there wasn't any material for them. So I did what I could, about one experiment a week maybe, with another day to discuss hypothesis, explanation, observation and conclusion, which I had taught them for lab sheets.

And on the other days I would bring in pictures I had cut out of magazines—any kind of pictures, like advertisements or landscapes. Once it was a picture of a man and a girl in heavy ski sweaters, against a snowy mountain background. The snow there . . . what was it? Something like rain, like water—another form of water maybe? Was it like anything they had ever seen before?

Yes, someone said, like those ice cubes from the fridge.

And did they think it was cold there? Yes, of course, look how cold the ice cubes had been. How else could they tell? What else was there in the picture that told them?

The clothes, one of them said.

63

Yes, the heavy ski sweater—look how warm those clothes were that they were wearing.

Was there any place in Tanganyika where there was snow?

Of course they knew that, Kilimanjaro, so it must be cold up there, too. And I read them a passage from a book about Rebmann, the German who had discovered Kilimanjaro, the first man to climb to the top, describing the Chagga, the tribe that lived on the slopes of the mountain. How they had told him about something white on top of the mountain and how they were all afraid to climb up to the top because of the cold. And how Rebmann, who had reached the top, had collected some snow and brought it down to a lower altitude.

And what did they think had happened to the snow?

It had melted.

Could they think of anything else that had melted this way? Yes, those ice cubes.

·   ·   ·

We usually ate a light lunch, since it became very hot in the afternoon and if you ate too much you'd just start getting drowsy. Meat with fruit and a salad, which Mbaliki would have on the table when we got back from classes.

Food was cheap, and easy to get, thanks to Mrs. Stark. We would just give Mbaliki our basket on Saturday morning and send him off to Tukuyu market with about five dollars' worth of shillings and the bus fare. He would come back in the afternoon with the basket filled with fruit, large fat oranges, mangoes, bananas, beans, cabbages, and potatoes. Being in the rainiest province had certain advantages. Fat juicy oranges for a penny. Ten little bananas for a penny. Mangoes and pineapples. No, we were never hurting for food.

Meat, we learned, was brought to the school twice a week for the boys. Each teacher would place his own special order for himself, so we ordered fifteen pounds a week since meat cost only fifteen cents a pound. It wasn't the best meat—usually we had to keep it in the fridge three or four days, it was so tough—but then again where else could you get meat for fifteen cents a pound?

The teachers, we noticed, would order only five or six pounds a week—that was all they could afford, which meant that they wouldn't eat meat more than once or maybe twice a week, as they all had wives and children to share it with.

As to water, Mbaliki went to the river for it, since the pump had broken down the first week, and brought it to the house in our bucket. Of course, we had to boil it, as God only knew how many cows and human beings did God only knew what in that river.

Then at two o'clock we would have assembly again, all the teachers shaking hands just as vehemently as in the morning, Good afternoon, Broo. How have you been since morning, how was lunch, how's the teaching? Who could believe we had seen each other just a few hours before?

And the band would start "Believe Me If All Those Endearing Young Charms" and off we'd go to inspection. Then marching to classes and teaching for the afternoon.

At three-thirty the bell would ring and the white shirts would run out to the assembly ground for their afternoon activity. We would be out there, Mike and I, in our shorts and sneakers, because the schedule called for sports three times a week. We ourselves had drawn up our special sports program for those three days, Mike working one week with the Standard 5's on baseball, batting and catching, just to give them a feel of the game, I with the 6's on basketball, passing and dribbling, switching to the next week, Mike teaching basketball to the 7's and I baseball to the 8's. We even talked about forming a baseball league and building a basketball court, measuring off a good length and finding some wooden backboards, maybe speaking to Kim Buck about shipping us some rims.

Except every day, it seemed, something went wrong. Either the Twak would come out and rail at the Standard 8 boys for the whole period about their exam, or there would be a special work project for the whole school, maybe cutting down trees for the teachers or carrying sacks of maize from Ushirika. Or we might actually follow the schedule for two or three days, getting two teams picked for the following day, but then the Twak might think that the 8's weren't getting enough math, and he would want to give them a special period that afternoon. Or that we hadn't had a debate in a long time, why not now?

Once I mentioned to him that it was very difficult organizing a sports program with all the schedule changes. He looked at me and began nodding his head, Yes, yes, very, very, he agreed.

And a few times at staff meetings I asked if maybe we could do

c

something about the afternoon schedule so that there wouldn't be so many changes—I thought we could work out a really good sports program—and I began explaining to them something about the baseball league that we were thinking of forming and the basketball court that we talking about building.

They would sit their nodding their heads and making noises, Mm, yes, mm, a very good idea. And the Twak would say, Yes, yes, very, very, we should, we should. Then someone would say, Yes, and what about the Photography Club or the Historical and Geographical Society or the Tribal Dances Organization, all of which had also been neglected. And that would start a discussion about What We Should Do Now. Maybe a thorough schedule change, someone would suggest. Yes, why not a complete new schedule to include all these activities? But first a committee had to be chosen to draw up the schedule. A week to get it drawn up. Another week for corrections and amendments. And then we wouldn't follow the new schedule any more than we had followed the old one.

So gradually we got used to the idea that we were not going to have any sports program. And what really hurt was that I had actually had those plans for the baseball league and the basketball court, for teaching them bunting and stealing, the lay-up and a jump shot. We could do it, I knew we could. And they would really enjoy it if they'd give us half a chance.

But what can you do? You had to be careful not to push too hard.

So we would dawdle the afternoon away, reading or correcting papers, watching the sun sliding toward the blue mountains, waiting for it to become a little cooler. Just before supper I would take my shower—Mbaliki would heat up two kettles of water for me each day and I would pour them into the bucket and stand under the two streams of water that would leak onto me, scrubbing furiously away. Then I would take another bucket of cold water, pouring it over me to wash it all off.

Supper was usually just before six, as Mbaliki liked to be home before dark. More meat, salad and potatoes.

Afterward we would bring out our baseball gloves, which fortunately we had both brought to Africa with us, and stand about ten yards apart, throwing and watching the sun sinking behind the blue

66

mountains, as though it were returning home behind its wall and lying down for the night.

The wives of the teachers would be sitting together on the grass in front of our houses, barefoot, in their bright, long dresses, sewing or plaiting mats. As they worked they would sing songs together in Kinyakusa, harmonizing, their little half-naked children at their breasts or sitting by their sides. Some of the children would be watching us throwing the ball, their mouths open in awe as we gathered the ball into our gloves. If we dropped one, or let one go past, they would all race for it, six or seven of them, squealing and pushing for the honor of returning it to us.

The wives would wave and jabber Kinyakusa at us as we threw back and forth, knowing of course that we couldn't understand them. And we would just say *Ndaga,* which would send them into howls of laughter.

They seemed so happy there, without any shoes or running water or electricity—what did they know about such things? But having their children running around near them, just the gentle loving way they held their babies to their breasts, singing their soft harmony in the coolness of the evening, the sun dipping behind the mountains —it was a picture I will always remember.

Night—and it was the nights that could be bad. Sitting from seven o'clock onward. What was there to do if you didn't read? At nine o'clock a light would come toward the window, the thudding of feet, a rap on the door. May I come in, sir? The boys were bringing us their exercise books to correct.

Exercise books, ninety a night, usually math and English daily and sometimes even science. What drudgery. But necessary. It was the least we could do for these kids.

So we would sit there late into the night, correcting papers, turning on the transistor we had bought, hearing the music of Radio Lourenço Marques or South Africa—the Four Seasons, the Rolling Stones, Jane from Capetown to Marty from Durban. From the girls at St. Cecilia's in Lourenço Marques. To Danny and Linda in Bulawayo. And thinking how far away their world seemed, how far from Ndumulu School, from the Twak, the staff meetings, the wives of the teachers sewing their mats and singing their harmony in their bare feet.

To sleep with the breeze coming in through the open window.

Listening for the scampering on the walls, for the dreaded *beep-beep,* which would mean climbing up on the roof the next day. But usually there were no *beeps*—instead it would be the hooting of an owl in a nearby tree, an animal crying from the forest, the deep *thump-thump* of a distant drum echoing across the valley, a wailing voice floating across the night. Wondering what they were doing out there—what were these noises? Why were they beating that drum? What did it all mean? How strange, how far away it all seemed, as far away as the voices of Lourenço Marques and South Africa—Ndumulu School and the voices of the night.

Weekends we would spend at Ushirika. We would walk together, all the *broos* of Ndumulu School, Saturday afternoon as soon as classes were over, and Sunday after church.

Church, where all the teachers and all the schoolboys would go every Sunday morning, up the road about a mile to a large brick building, or if it was very hot, to a clearing dotted with banana trees, where rows of benches had been assembled, where people sat in their Sunday best, in their black tuxedo coats and bright orange dresses, with bright sandals. And I recalled how Mr. Twakatulu had told us that first time we had gone to Ushirika that there were many Christians in the area.

They were of all different sects, Moravians, Lutherans, Baptists, Seventh Day Adventists, Catholics—the Africans called them Romans—it didn't seem to make any difference. Even Mr. Ngulu, who had two wives, would come. What sect was he, I wondered. A Mormon, perhaps.

Each of them would be given a hymnbook with songs and psalms written in Nyakusa. And they would sing with all their hearts, as loud as they could—if volume was any criterion, they couldn't miss getting to heaven—sitting there under the banana trees, Nyakusa words to the tune of "Onward Christian Soldiers." With an old man, the preacher, in a long white gown leading them from up on the high ground, waving his arms and exhorting them in Nyakusa. What was it he was saying? Something about the suffering of Jesus, a parable—maybe to lead a good Christian life?

From church along the road to Daniel Mwamatuma's Tanganyika Bar where we *broos* would huddle around one of the tables, doubling up on chairs. Agnes would bring us bowls of pombe—she was usually drunk by the time we got there—and would spill it on us as she placed the pombe on the table. They would all yell at her indignantly, yet indulgently, as she began to wipe up, while they fondled her and she laughed a drunken chuckle.

The bowl would go round and round, and by this time I had nearly perfected the art of pretending to take great big gulps but really only sipping tiny drops, all the while holding my breath so I couldn't smell the brew. As we drank, villagers who knew us would come up, *Oogonile, ndaga*, and we would welcome them to our bowl, *Isaga*, which always seemed to please them very much, while other villagers whom we didn't know would be standing around goggling at us, no doubt the first white people they had ever seen drinking local stuff.

And soon we would be slapping palms and calling to each other, *broo, broo* and people seeing us this way, enjoying ourselves, would point to us and laugh. Women were coming in to Mwama tuma's now, wearing bright dresses with bright green shoes, standing by the teachers and whispering to them, while the teachers fondled their thighs. Soon they would get up and leave, one by one. Mr. Ngubile explained that that's what the one-room huts were for —the entertaining pleasures of the life-ists, because so many wicked women came here to Ushirika.

We slapped palms on that. Ushirika, the Babylon of the Southern Highlands.

And what would happen is that after one hour they would all have gone, all the teachers, and a strange new group of people would have taken their places around the bowl. And Mike and I would continue drinking, laughing and smiling, listening to their Nyakusa, neither knowing their names nor understanding what they were saying.

Soon we might get a little restless and we would walk outside, past people sitting together in groups or standing and holding hands in that gentle way they had, which was really nice if you thought about it. They would shout to us, *Broo, Broo, Isaga,* or *Karibu*, which is welcome in Nyakusa and Swahili, asking us to sip from their bowls.

We would wave and laugh and call back to them—it was nice to know that they felt they knew us well enough to call out to us like that. And we would join them for a quick sip, always remembering to keep moving, as they always wanted you to sit there with them until the bowl was finished.

There would be Daudi with no teeth, who sold sticks of roasted meat just outside of Mwamatuma's, and Eustace, short and balding, who brought us bread in the morning which he baked himself. They would pull at our sleeves, trying to lead us to their homes, they always had food they wanted to give us.

Usually we would stop over to see Mbaliki who lived just across the street. His wife made her own pombe so there were always people inside his house drinking. They would always be so happy to see us, he would stand there smiling like a little child, his long black mustache wet at the tip with pombe, and his wife would bring us their babies to show us. And they would bring chairs for us, and offer us pombe, it was all so nice and kind of them, and I would call him the Leek. Then they would bring us food, meat, because the Leek knew that's what we really liked. And it always touched me when he did that—it was probably their whole supply of meat for the week, maybe even for the month. And of course we would never take it. But that's what it was about these people, not just Mbaliki, they were all like that, they had next to nothing, but they were willing to share with you all that they had.

When there was no pombe at Mwamatuma's the teachers would take us to another bar across the street. It wasn't really a bar at all, they said, but a club, a long bamboo building with a counter along one side behind which little old women stood with their *debes* of pombe. Each would thrust her cup over the counter at you as you passed, and you were supposed to taste them all, sometimes five or six cups, and then decide which brew you liked best—as if there could be such a thing—and order a bowl of that one.

Throughout the rest of the hut were tables and benches close together with old men in torn clothes sitting there dipping their faces into the bowls, with beards and mustaches dripping wet with muddy pombe. Some without shoes, some with shoes with holes, some with one shoe with no laces, some with different colored socks. And all calling to us as we tried to make our way through them out the side door, *Isaga, isaga,* welcome to our bowl. Was it because we were strangers or white, or teachers, that they asked us? Did they want to prove to themselves that we would really drink with them? Was it to build their image in their eyes? But it was good of them to ask us, kind of them, and so you did your best to join them for a sip. You felt it would be impolite to refuse.

So the weekends would pass this way, each Saturday and each

Sunday, the *broos* of Ndumulu School, with Sunday mornings at church, singing hymns under the banana trees, and Ushirika, the same groups of people, the same drinking, drinking all Saturday and all Sunday, drinking from Saturday afternoon until Sunday night.

We'd usually begin to head for school about evening, the two of us, Mike and I, as the other teachers were never to be found once they had gone off with the wicked women. Past drunks staggering and weaving now, urinating and defecating on the side of the road. Past people singing to themselves, falling into bushes, staggering, *Broo, broo*, as we passed, *Broo, broo*. Past people sitting by their huts, all with bowls, calling, waving to us that there was pombe there, *Mwalimu, mwalimu, isaga, isaga,* old men and old women, in rags and wisps of clothing, all with their bowls of pombe.

Night coming on, the shadows of banana trees, the glow of fires in the huts on the side of the road, the high-pitched wails and chants that swept out into the night. The faint beginnings of the drum . . . wondering where these noises came from, what did they mean? How easy it was to let your imagination wander and drift there in the dusk. What was behind that next big tree or around the next bend in the road? And then the voice of a radio coming from one of the huts, you could hear it faintly now, Ricky Nelson:

> *I'm a travelin' man*
> *Made a lot of stops,*
> *All over the world.*

And thinking back to that first time drinking pombe at Bwana Mbulu's, the centuries-old way of life of these people, for generations and generations, all shattered by the world of today, the voice of the present, Ricky Nelson and Elvis Presley.

Sometimes we would meet Mr. Biboko as he staggered home by himself. What would happen to him is that he would become drunk and begin arguing with villagers saying that he was from Tanga where the people were more civilized than the Nyakusa. The teachers would become insulted and angry at this and would leave, but the villagers would stay and call him names. And Mr. Biboko would tell them that he was just smarter and better-educated than they, that his tribe was better than the Nyakusa. And, of course, that would only make them angrier, and then more names and more insults about the Nyakusa, and finally even the villagers would get up and leave.

But on Monday it would all seem to have been forgotten, and they would go around shaking hands with one another—Good morning, *broo,* Good morning, *Babu,* laughing and slapping palms as though nothing had happened at all. I couldn't quite make it out.

Once a month, on the same date each month, there would be a cinema. As it grew dark, a sound truck would pull up at Ushirika, where the whole town and surrounding villages had all descended, and they would put up a giant screen.

Imagine my surprise the first time, when I saw an old, old news-reel, British, I think, the King and a parade, and then a conference of some kind, with the voice in English—while everyone laughed and howled. Then a movie short about the making of milk—a farm in Northern England, milking the cows by machine, pasteurizing it—and the villagers standing next to me, mouths agape, hanging on each movement.

Then the main feature, and Mr. Ngubile saying I was going to be surprised. It was a Western, an old John Wayne movie, John Wayne on a white horse, jumping and heading off a runaway stage-coach, a blond girl and her father being run off the ranch by rus-tlers, some riding, shooting, a couple of fights—you know, the whole bit. But how they loved it, how they howled as John Wayne jumped from his horse to the stage, how they roared when he knocked the rustlers down, when they tumbled over. How they laughed when John Wayne kissed the blond girl, how they smiled when he rode off on his white horse, the girl waving heartbrokenly after him . . . until next month. And the villagers running over to us, Mike and me, asking us if that was how America really was, and we said something about that's the way it used to be a long time ago.

Once I asked the Twak if perhaps the schoolboys could go to the cinema, it would be a wonderful experience for them. Not just the Western but the newsreel and the feature. Maybe they could even pick up some of the English. But he said no, that it would be bad for the discipline.

Definitely not, very, very.

·    ·    ·

One Saturday as I was returning from Ushirika, I found Mr. Biboko weaving all over the road. He was saying, *Broo, broo,* my young *broo,* that he had been arguing with some people at Ushirika, and that they feared him because of his intelligence, that the Nyakusa were really a very uncivilized and savage people, weren't they? And with that he fell headfirst into a pothole in the road. As I pulled him out, he told me how lucky it was that he had found me because he could help me get home.

When we reached the school he said that he had something he wanted to say to the boys. They were all in the dining room—did I want to come with him?

Maybe I should, to make sure he reached there in one piece.

As we approached we could see in through the window. One little boy was standing on the platform waving his arms excitedly as he spoke in Swahili. And all the boys were listening very intently, their mouths open, their eyes wide, hanging on every word the little boy was saying. As we slipped inside, Mr. Biboko whispered to me that they were having their social talks, where each boy could speak about anything he wished to the rest of the boys.

The little one up there was speaking very quickly now—how is it that a little boy like that has no fear of speaking in front of others, no shyness, isn't the least bit afraid—as though he were just talking to some of his own little friends?

Mr. Biboko began edging toward the front of the room, and I followed. The boys saw us now and began to stand, the whole dining room was standing now, the little boy stopped speaking in the middle of his sentence, looking bewildered. Mr. Biboko walked up on the platform, I followed, and suddenly the little boy ran off the platform down among his friends.

The boys were still standing so Mr. Biboko motioned them to be seated. He began speaking to them in Swahili, quickly, very quickly, and of course I couldn't understand what he was saying. He was raising his voice now, waving his arms, and suddenly he gave out with a great loud burp and broke into a short chuckle. I realized only then for the first time that he was very drunk, and it occurred to me that perhaps I shouldn't be here with him. And I noticed the boys fidgeting in their seats, looking at each other, as Mr. Biboko went on, yelling now, screaming at them.

Suddenly the door opens, the Twak is standing there, Mr. Twakatulu, you can see his long black mustache, his eyes and teeth flashing, and maybe it is the darkness, but I have never seen him this way before. Mr. Biboko stops cold, his mouth hanging open, and the boys, sensing something is wrong, turn and see the Twak standing at the back. The dining room rises en masse, not a word, only the sound of benches scraping.

Now with a sweep of his hand, Mr. Twakatulu dismisses the boys from the dining room. Still he does not move but stands there in the doorway as they file past him without a sound. And after the boys have gone, Mr. Biboko slinks sheepishly past him out the door, just as the boys have done, not a word, like a dog with his tail between his legs.

So I am left there alone with him, Mr. Twakatulu, and he tells me he has been standing there outside listening and that he believes I do not know what Mr. Biboko has been saying. He says that Mr. Biboko is a very wicked man, that he has been telling the boys very bad things— He is going to take my place as headmaster because I will be sent away—and he begins nodding his head furiously.

He goes on that Mr. Biboko is very bad when he drinks, very dangerous. That sometimes when he is drunk he tells the boys about his magic from Tanga and the boys become afraid. Now the Twak pulls out a letter and starts waving it in front of me, telling me how just before Mike and I had come, Mr. Biboko was drunk one night and had entered Mr. Mwadunda's house when he wasn't there. Only his wife was there, and when Mr. Mwadunda returned home, he found them together.

This letter, he says, is from the Regional Education Officer, it is a warning to Mr. Biboko that if he drinks again, steps will be taken, and he begins to nod his head furiously again up and down.

So I tell you, I warn you, I beg you, beware of this man. I know that you did not mean anything by this tonight, that you really did not have any part, that you did not know what he was saying. But beware of him, I tell you.

And suddenly he strode off, leaving me standing there by myself looking after him as he faded into the night.

I smiled to myself. A nervous smile perhaps. The Twak had a certain dignity about him all his own.

 *     *     *

Then it was my turn to be the duty master. Which meant that I would be in charge of the running of the school for the week, seeing that the boys got up in time in the morning, that they did their jobs and listened to the prefects, that the school was clean, that there were no fights, no seriously ill boys, that the meals were cooked on time, because, they said, the cooks had a habit of not showing up in the mornings.

The schedule said that the boys must be up at six and doing their exercises—whatever that was. I was a little late the first morning because it was still dark, and as I approached the dormitories, I heard noise—shouts—and quick I thought there was something wrong, a fight maybe.

But as I drew nearer, I saw it wasn't coming from the dormitories, it was from down on the field. I could see them now, standing in four large circles, the whole school—you could only see their outlines there in the darkness. There was a boy in the center of each circle, leading them, they were doing our exercises, the ones we had taught the Standard 8 boys. Jumping jacks now, figures jumping about in the darkness, shouting out the numbers—One, two, three, four—as we had taught them to do. And the boy in the center screaming at them, Get those knees up, higher, as they all began running in place, with him screaming, No slackers, just as they had heard me do it, in the same stentorian voice. Now running at one boy, hollering, You, you, you.

After their exercises they began their jobs. Some sweeping the dormitories, some sweeping the paths, using bunches of leaves which they had pulled down from trees, others straightening the beds, or cleaning the classrooms or the dining hall. And the thing was that they each had some allotted job to do, even the little Standard 5 boys, who would pick up papers or prune the flowers in front of the dormitories, while the prefects walked around overseeing them.

At seven they lined up outside the dining hall, where some boys were stirring three barrels of some kind of watery cereal that looked like oatmeal. They used thick wooden sticks to stir them while the boys waited in long lines, each holding a cup. The prefects would take five or six cups at a time, scoop the cereal into them and hand them back to the boys, who would begin to drink it—that's how watery it was. When they finished they would run down to the river to clean their cups, as the pump was still not working.

Then the bell would bong—there were special boys, I saw,

whose job it was to bong the bell—and they would all race to assembly, squealing like little pigs as I chased after them, stick in
hand, screaming at them, Gettamuvon. Then the band would play
the national anthem as the Twak would bounce out, yelling at the
Standard 8's calling out certain names. They would come forward
and lie down in pushup position, the Twak looking at me, waiting
for me to beat them with the stick, the way the duty master was
supposed to do.

So I did. I had to. Four strokes for each.

Then the band banging away, the Ndumulu army marching off to
class. . . .

At lunch the boys would squeeze into the undersized dining room,
each of them with a bowl of beans and gravy sauce and some kind
of grain meal called *dona,* which looked something like paste with
little seeds in it. They would take the *dona* with their hands and dip
it into the bowl, as we had done with the *ugali* at Mr. Biboko's,
and I would walk through, tasting it, making sure it was cooked all
right—as if I could tell. When they finished, down to the river
again to wash out their bowls, and the girls began sweeping the dining room with their branch-brooms under the eye of the dining-hall
prefects.

In the afternoon, when the three-thirty bell gonged, they would
run to the assembly ground and go off in their little groups, a prefect to each group, for work around the school. Cutting the grass,
cleaning the dining hall again, washing the pots and dishes again as
there might be some dirty ones left lying about. And I began to see
what Mr. Biboko had meant when he said that each teacher was
the president of 360 boys. For they would each collect groups of
boys, two or three, five or ten, twenty if they needed them, to work
in the bookstore, to carry their sacks of maize from Ushirika, to
chop their trees, to wash and iron their clothes. And the boys
would do these jobs uncomplainingly, almost willingly, it seemed.

At five o'clock they would be lined up in front of the dining hall
as prefects dished out cups of tea—the schedule called for tea at
four-thirty but they always seemed to run half an hour late.
Some boys might be playing soccer, which they called football.
They played in bare feet, these boys, and they could kick the ball
forty and fifty yards.

Sometimes the Twak would go out there with them. He had been
a championship player a few years ago, we had heard, and he had

once played for the Tanganyika national team. Now, he said, he was too old to play any more, only once in a while, so he would go out with the boys, refereeing, coaching and kicking, when the spirit moved him, yelling and screaming instructions and advice at them at the top of his lungs.

Then a boy comes up to me, Asegelile Mwamenda, and he says that his money has been stolen, two twenty-shilling notes. I'm not certain what to do, so I tell Mr. Biboko, whose house is nearby, and he sends a boy out to the field to call the Twak, and the Twak runs over to where we are standing, and suddenly I hear the bell ringing, *bong, bong, bong,* hard and fast, the call of *hatari,* the warning bell, danger.

Now the boys start running to the assembly ground as fast as they can. They seem to come from everywhere, from classrooms, from dormitories, from down the valley, over the hill, from the woods where they are not permitted to be, like the rats following the Pied Piper of Hamelin, as they answer to the call of the *hatari* bell.

They stand there in their lines as the Twak stalks up to them, his white teeth gleaming behind his black mustache, glaring at them as he glared at Mr. Biboko that night in the dining room, roaring at them, cursing at them in Swahili, *Wanafunzi wabaya.* He stops and begins asking them now, very sternly, Has anybody seen or heard about this boy's money? Does anyone think he knows who might have taken it?

One boy raises his hand and says a name, very timidly, Afyosisye Mwangabula. The Twak calls out, Afyosisye Mwangabula. No answer. Someone says he thinks he has gone to the river.

So the Twak sends the prefects down there after him, and they run off in a herd, twenty-five of them, while the boys stand there without a sound as the Twak paces back and forth in front of them like a caged animal, his hands behind his back, his eyes burning.

Soon the prefects return. They are dragging a boy, Afyosisye Mwangabula, and they throw him at the feet of the Twak like dogs presenting their master with a prize morsel. The Twak begins to question him, as Afyosisye shakes his head. No, he doesn't know anything about it, he was only washing his clothes at the river.

But the Twak doesn't seem to hear him, he is yelling at him now, and he calls out to the boy whose money has been stolen. Asegelile Mwamenda, How much was it?

77

Two twenty-shilling notes.

Now the Twak stands right over Afyosisye Mwangabula and I notice for the first time how little the boy is and that he is shaking with fear. Suddenly Mr. Twakatulu slaps him across the face, a sudden sharp crack, and the boy involuntarily clutches the side of his face and begins to cry. And the Twak screams at him again, You *shenzi,* you *Changuku,* as the boy shakes his head, Please, please, he doesn't know anything about it, why is he being beaten?

And anyone can see that the poor little kid is telling the truth, that he cannot possibly know anything about the money, he is so little and so afraid. Why can't the Twak see it, what kind of a man can he be, doing that to a shaking little boy?

Then the Twak asks him if he has any money and the boy shakes his head, No, and the Twak pulls him to him and begins to search his clothes and his pockets. Nothing.

Suddenly he calls to the prefects to bring the boy's box here, he wants to examine it, and Afyosisye Mwangabula goes rigid. In a few minutes they return, bringing the box, a large wooden one with a lock, and the schoolboys crowd around it as close as they can. Mr. Twakatulu begins going through it—a pair of shorts, a shirt, some notebooks, a textbook, a spoon, pair of trousers, some old coins, a white shirt—throwing each item on the ground as he finishes with it.

Then between two pages of a book down at the bottom, hidden carefully away, there it is. Two twenty-shilling notes. Well, I'll be damned. This little kid actually has stolen the money. All his crying and shaking his head and pleading, it was all an act. He had certainly fooled me, all right. But not the Twak.

Now Mr. Twakatulu lifts up his hand with the two twenty-shilling notes for the boys to see, and they gasp and draw back. And suddenly Afyosisye Mwangabula tries to escape, but the prefects are there to grab him and they drag him back. The Twak is livid now as the boy cowers on the ground beneath him. He orders the prefects to get him some sticks, strong lean ones, and they run off while he takes off his coat and rolls up his sleeves, as the boy lies weeping on the ground.

They have to hold the boy—he is squirming so—as the Twak brings his hand down, the stick swishing through the air. One. Two. Three. Four strokes. The boy is sobbing now, whining. Five. Six. Seven. Eight. Now the Twak calls for a razor, and one of the prefects comes forward and begins shaving little Afyosisye's head, while the boy just sits there on the ground, his whole body shaking with sobs, but with no sound, with tears running down his face and falling on pieces of his black curly hair lying on the ground beside him.

At night inspection, I come by after ten and have to turn the Standard 8 boys out of the classroom . . . they are still studying. Through the dormitories, each lighted only by a small hurricane lamp, as the prefects escort me. Bed after bed on both sides of the corridor. The boys asleep, each wrapped in a skimpy blanket on a thin straw mat that serves as a mattress, rolled up tight like little balls or lumps of soggy clay, their whole bodies under the covers, with only the rise and fall of their breathing. I pass out the door into the next dormitory, through all four of them, and back to my house, as the school sleeps.

Next day I see the boys playing, Afyosisye Mwangabula with his bald head running around and laughing, and with him Asegelile Mwamenda, the boy whose money he had stolen. They are playing together like the best of friends. And I can't help thinking of Mr. Biboko at Ushirika—how the teachers would all become angry at him and leave him, but then on Monday at assembly would all be shaking hands again, *Broo, broo,* laughing together as though nothing had happened. I don't pretend that I understand.

Social evening for the boys. As I approached the dining hall I heard a great noise and could see figures bobbing and weaving through the window. There in front was a group of boys from Standard 8, singing at the top of their lungs, Rock, rock, rock tonight, while next to them stood three boys beating drums with their hands, *boom, boom, boom,* one-two, one-two, the same kind of rhythm we would hear at night coming from across the valley.

The whole dining-room floor was alive with figures, boys dancing by themselves or with each other, each of them caught up entirely by the music, the *boom, boom, boom,* taking little steps with their bare feet, moving with a slow catlike grace to the shouting of the singers, Rock, rock, rock tonight, hearing nothing but the music.

One little boy who couldn't have been more than ten years old swept by, his hands folded behind his back, his head tilted upward to the ceiling, his eyes staring off into space. He was half smiling, half in the dining room and half in his own little world, and you knew that in his mind he was the only person in that room.

And they would dance by themselves or with a partner, two big ones together, graceful and gentle despite their size, and two little ones, while the singers howled, singing in Nyakusa now, the drums pounding away *thump thump thump, boom boom boom,* the dancers making no sound, only their bodies moving, their white teeth grinning, their eyes half closed. And two little ones floating past, holding hands ever so lightly, a group of them in a line, each holding onto the waist of the boy in front of him, singing as they moved their feet in little one-two one-two steps, the *boom boom boom* of the big bass drum.

· · ·

Quite accidentally, while I was hunting for some science equipment, I found a carton of books hidden away in the back of one of the cupboards in the office. There were ten sets of them with fifty books to a set, books like a simplified *David Copperfield, Treasure Island, Gulliver's Travels.* And they were almost exactly the right reading level for the boys in Class 7.

So Mike and I divided them up between us, half for 7A, the other half for 7B. I started with the simplest, which was *Gulliver's Travels,* giving the boys two weeks to read it, making them take a test and turn in a book report on it at the end of that time.

The boys' eyes lit up as I showed them the books. A special treat, I told them, their own book for two weeks. And they thought it was some great gift, something I must have brought with me from America. They just couldn't wait for class to be over so that they could read them. In fact some of them didn't wait, they would be reading as I talked about nouns and pronouns, becoming so engrossed that I could tiptoe over to them and roar in their ears, And what do you think you are doing? And they shot up in their chairs and then looked at me very sheepishly.

I started off with very easy questions on the tests, sticking to details such as, What was the name of the island that Gulliver first landed on? or Why couldn't Gulliver move when he woke up? And they were really quite something with details, these boys; somehow they didn't forget a thing. Like when I asked, What did they feed

Gulliver the first day? they all knew the exact number of cows and pigs, even the number of bottles of milk he drank. I guess that had really inpressed them.

I also had them making speeches, each boy giving a two-minute talk in front of the class on any subject he liked, while the rest of them sat there ready to notice any and all mistakes the speaker might make, ears cocked, on the edge of their seats, ready to throw up their hands the moment they heard something that was just the slightest bit incorrect.

The first time round the speakers all had trouble, falling all over themselves with simple mistakes, saying things like, He came next week, or I went to the store to bought some food—to the delight of the audience, who would shoot their hands up in glee.

But by the second time you could see the improvement. Slowly, carefully—simple vocabulary, granted—but they were speaking correctly for the most part, without too many mistakes, a brand of reasonably comprehensible English.

And in math too they were coming along. It's truly amazing what practice will do. Not that they still didn't make mistakes. Not infrequently I'd see things like nine times nine equals seventy-two. But there was a difference, a marked one—the mistakes were being cut down. All the drill, that's what was doing it. Some of them were beginning to finish their tests on time, four or five of them sometimes turning in perfect papers.

But it was in science that I was having my greatest difficulties. We could do an experiment—they could see it for themselves, they would understand it, I was sure they did—yet somehow they weren't really convinced. We boiled water in a little pan I had brought to class, and I told them to watch the steam going into the air, pointing out after some time that the water level of the pan had dropped. Why did they think that was?

One boy, Fedson Mwandemele, said, It is the steam, which is really water, that has gone out.

Yes, I said, the water when it is boiled passes off as steam. It changes its form when you boil it just as when we freeze it, it changes its form and becomes ice. So that the steam is really the water in the pan which has escaped into the air.

And they sat there, the boys, looking up into the air. They seemed to expect to see the steam hanging there in space like a balloon or a great cloud filled with water. And as I went out, I felt

81

them looking at me with the same sidelong glance as when the ice had melted, as if there was some part of the trick that I wasn't telling them. And I heard some of them whispering the word *uchawi,* which is Swahili for witchcraft.

One day I asked Mr. Ngubile about it, whether the boys really did believe in witchcraft. He looked at me very strangely as if to say, Don't you believe in witchcraft? Then he asked me, Isn't there witchcraft in America? And he began telling the story of a good friend of his who had recently died, because he hadn't paid some money he owed to an old Indian. The Indian had bewitched him, Mr. Ngubile said. That's why he had died.

I stood there looking at him in disbelief, he couldn't really believe that, not Mr. Ngubile, he was the most intelligent of them all. It was he who had coined the words local stuff and life-ists. He was an intelligent, educated man.

But it's true, *broo,* he said. It's really true, I tell you, *broo.*

The Twak had been standing there listening to us, and now he began telling this story about Mr. Biboko. It seemed that when the Twak had first come here to Ndumulu School at the end of last year, Mr. Biboko invited him to his house for a cup of tea. But instead of pouring the tea right there in front of us, the Twak said, Mr. Biboko's wife poured it in the kitchen, where I couldn't see it, and she brought in the cups already full. And I had already heard stories about Mr. Biboko's magic, the Twak said—here Mr. Ngubile nodded, a nod I inferred to mean that he had heard some stories. And I was about to drink it, the Twak went on, when suddenly—and here the Twak started bouncing up and down, waving his arms and screaming, *Kilivunjika, kilivunjika*—the cup broke, the cup broke, and it was only Mungu, God, that had saved him, because there must have been some poison in the cup, how else could it have cracked like that?

Why had his cup cracked and not Mr. Biboko's, he said very scientifically, if it wasn't poisoned? And Mr. Ngubile nodded, looking at me as if to say, See, *broo,* what do you think of that?

And I thought of poor Mr. Biboko. Maybe he had insulted the Nyakusa, maybe even he had made up some fanciful stories about Tanga magic. But a poisoner! How hurt he would have felt to hear a story like this about him. And it occurred to me that here was Mr. Ngubile, his good friend, life-ist number one, standing here this way and nodding to these stories about him. Wasn't that funny.

How could he be his friend and believe these stories about him? What was it about these people?

And it also occurred to me that whenever I had any of them to my house I would make sure to pour the tea right in front of them.

· · ·

Then the rains came. First it would be at four o'clock every afternoon when the black clouds would come from behind the blue mountains and fade everything into a bleary gray, and the thunder would shake through the sky like an animal roaring, it would last so long.

You could see the mist from the mountains slipping in behind the boys' dormitories, covering them in a shroud of gray, and then moving across to our houses. And the rain would start, large drops splattering on the roof, and suddenly a streak of lightning would be flashing through the gray, over the mountains. Pounding on our roofs now, the house shaking under the blows, the wind whistling through the corrugations and sweeping under the edges of the roof, banging the flaps of tin.

A burst of thunder, the shrieks of the teachers' little children as they ran to the safety of their mothers. The day pupils in the classrooms, standing in the doorway peering out at the rain, waiting for it to let up so they could make their way home.

It could come every day now, at the same time, and it would be over in not much more than an hour. And after it stopped you could see the white wisps of clouds hanging on the mountains as they began to lift.

It was the *masika,* the heavy rains, and it would rain a little harder and a little longer each day. The day pupils, standing at the doorway of their classrooms, waiting for a break in the rain which wouldn't come— finally they would have to walk home, each with a giant banana leaf over his head. And how much could that protect them when they had to walk four and five miles?

Now when it stopped it would only be for a little while. It would rain all night, you'd go to sleep with the house shaking, the wind flapping the edges of the roof. In the morning it would still be drizzling, the whole sky gray and foggy, and sometimes you couldn't even see over to the classrooms.

It would go on through the morning, maybe letting up around eleven or twelve o'clock, and some days you might even be able to catch a glimpse of the sun for a few minutes. Then as the afternoon came, the gray-black clouds would begin creeping over the mountains, a line of lightning flashing above them, a sudden clap of thunder. And the little children would shriek as they ran to their mothers, the first big drops splattering on the roof. It had begun again.

One afternoon Kim Buck appeared in his Land Rover. It was the first time we had seen him since that night at Martin Martinson's. He brought a portable movie projector that ran on paraffin, a screen and some films that USIS had sent. They were ours for a month, he said. Then he would come back and collect them.

The Twak was very excited about it, and he arranged for the whole school to come that night to the dining hall. Mr. Mwambigila said that he was expert on these projectors, that he had learned at the Teacher Training College, so he would run ours. And I thought of what a welcome break it would be from the nights we were spending, because it was the nights that could begin to get you, sitting from seven o'clock on, just the two of us, reading, waiting for exercise books to come, listening to the radio.

Now inside the dining room, the first film was some kind of travelogue about America, about some Tanganyikan who gets off the plane in New York and goes on a bus across the country. They showed some national parks, some shots of New York and Washington and San Francisco, and finally his getting back on the plane and waving to all the American friends he had made, who were standing there with big smiles—typical USIS, but they loved it.

The next one was a rodeo, modern cowboys in spurs and chaps and hats. They all recognized the cowboys from Ushirika and a great roar went up when they first appeared on the screen. They'd open the gate and you'd see the cowboys bouncing on the broncs and the bulls, all of them being quickly thrown, except for one cowboy who kept bouncing higher and higher in the air as the bronc reared and kicked, to a crescendo of howls from the boys each time he went up. But the cowboy wouldn't fall, he stayed right on, and each time he flew a little higher up into the air, the howls grew louder, until finally he was thrown and the place broke out into a bedlam of shrieks that you thought would blow the tin roof right off.

Then there was one about Dick Tiger, whom they all knew as he was a famous African champion. They would howl as he went

84

through his exercises, skipping rope cross-handed, hitting the punching bag, and of course in the ring. But there really wasn't too much action in the film, not very much actual fighting, it was mostly about how he came to be champion from his poor background, through hard training and hard work.

But there was one scene in there that was really great—although of course it didn't get any howls. It showed Dick Tiger getting up at four A.M. to do his roadwork, the city all dark and sleeping, no one on the streets, only Dick Tiger running down Central Park South past the Plaza and Trader Vic's in his sweat clothes, his trainers pacing him in a car a few steps ahead of him on the empty streets of New York.

Next day the Twak called a staff meeting to tell us that he had decided to show the films again that night and every night that week. This time many of the villagers came, all the old men and old women in their ragged torn clothes, with younger children who perhaps had never seen a film before. They would fill the dining room and we'd have to stand at the back, and soon it became so crowded that there was not enough room for all of them, so the overflow would have to stand outside in the rain peering through the windows.

Every night that week we showed the films, and every night the dining hall was filled with villagers. Each night the same film, and the same howls at the same places, the cowboys being thrown off their broncs, the crescendo of howls as the lone cowboy shot into the air.

And the rain shattering on the roof, the wind shaking the building, the shadows of those people standing outside peering in through the window, with only banana leaves covering their heads as the rain pounded at them. But still they came, with the film running, the sound drowned out by the patter of rain and the shrieks.

Then the Twak decided that we should show the films every night until our four weeks were up. So we did until one night the projector blew and Mr. Mwambigila couldn't figure out what had happened, and we never could get it started again.

Later Kim Buck told us that he had sent the projector to Nairobi, but that they couldn't fix it there either, because we had been playing it without oil the whole time, and the projector had blown clear through. He said that he wasn't bringing us anything else as we didn't know how to take care of things.

So that ended the films. And it was back to reading and exercise books for us, and for the Africans whatever they did with themselves at night.

.    .    .

Just after the projector blew, we had a meeting and were discussing something about whether we should all go to pay a visit to Mr. Ndendulu, whose son had just died. Mr. Ndendulu, they told Mike and me, had been a teacher at Ndumulu last year. What they were discussing was whether we teachers should all go or whether we should send one or two representatives, as his village was about five miles away.

I took it to mean that they didn't want us to go with them for some reason, but Mike whispered that they didn't think we wanted to go as it was so far. So we made sure to tell them that by all means we wanted to go if that was the case.

So we set out that afternoon—sure enough, that had been the case. At Ushirika we met some other teachers from other schools who were also going, and I marveled at the way they could all just leave school for the day. Somehow I had thought this only happened at Ndumulu.

We cut down a narrow path that wiggled down valleys and up the backs of mountains. Because of the rains the ground was very wet and muddy and you'd have to run when you went downhill so as not to lose your footing and find yourself on your rear caked with mud. Then going up you would also have to run because if you didn't you would get stuck in the mud without enough momentum to get to the top, and you'd have to walk back down to the bottom and start all over again.

As we approached the top of one hill, it seemed to level out, a small clearing ahead, and there was a great noise, a kind of shriek or wail, and there on the ground was a group of women, there must have been a hundred of them, sitting on their haunches, wailing in high-pitched cries, AAAHHHOOO, AAAHHHUUU, AAAHHHOOO, AAA-HHHUUU—very old women with black cloths around their skinny bodies, some wearing nothing over their breasts, which would hang down, drooping, worn by how many years and how many children. They took no notice of us as we stepped among them, except perhaps to increase their wail. And it was the most horrible, fright-

86

ening, lamentable cry coming from these thin little old women, you wanted to put cotton in your ears, anything just to shut it out.

We passed among them to some old men seated on logs, drinking bowls of pombe. They all stood up as we approached, *Oogonile, oogonile, ndaga, ndaga.* Everyone seemed to know everyone so we acted as though we did too, as they made room for us on the log and passed us the bowl.

Two old women came over and lay down on the ground, *Oogonile, ndaga.* Mr. Mwadunda said that they were Mr. Ndendulu's mothers. Then some other women who had been wailing came over to us and lay down, and all the while the wailing continued.

A short man with a round face waddled over. This was Mr. Ndendulu and he was thanking us all for having come. He told Mike and me that he had heard a lot about us, and said thank you again. Then he went off with Mr. Mwadunda and Mr. Mwaisunga, and they sat down apart from the others.

I asked someone how old the child had been and what he had died of, and they answered that he was five years old, his firstborn. No one knew what it was, some feared he had been bewitched, and I wondered if they had ever taken him to a doctor.

Now the women were all coming over, they carried pots of food on their heads. Another woman came and knelt down in front of us, turning her face away as we greeted her. It was Mrs. Ndendulu, the mother of the child, they said.

Later the Twak pointed up at the sky, and said we had better be leaving before the afternoon rains. So we got up and started for home, all of us except Mr. Mwadunda and Mr. Mwaisunga, who remained sitting there with Mr. Ndendulu. The Twak explained that they had both lost their sons last year, and that they would spend the night here with Mr. Ndendulu.

I looked around me for the last time. There must have been two hundred people there in that clearing, all having come to pay their respects to Mr. Ndendulu for his little dead son. I walked over to say goodbye to him to tell him how sorry I was. I wanted to say something more, but what can you say to someone who has just lost his son?

# II

THEN IT WAS THE cold season. You don't think of Africa as being cold, but here in the Southern Highlands you'd find yourself putting on a sweater as it grew dark and then a coat and on toward ten o'clock a blanket around your feet. We'd sit huddled up late at night, the blankets around our knees, correcting papers or hearing the faraway voices on the radio, our little charcoal burner, which we had bought for ten shillings, in the middle of the floor. In the morning there would be frost on the ground.

Mbaliki had an old black coat—a lady's coat—that his cousin from Rhodesia had sent him, and I'd see him in the mornings with it wrapped tightly around his skinny body, with the white tennis shoes I had given him, and his long black mustache.

The boys had nothing. Only their shorts and short-sleeved shirts, standing at assembly in the mornings, barefoot, shivering, as the sun hadn't risen high enough yet to warm the ground, with great cold sores around their mouths and lips. They were always sick now, it seemed—malaria, dysentery—with maybe a quarter of them out of class at a time. You'd find them in the dormitories, each wrapped under one skimpy blanket, a large lump there on the bed.

Getting up at six in the morning, pitch-black now, with the wind whistling through them—the schedule said they had to do exercises —their bare feet on the early morning frost. The day students getting up even before six and walking five miles to school in the early morning blackness.

It was also the dying season. That was the word Mbaliki used.

Due to the cold of course, he would explain. There seemed to be a death in every village, mostly old people and babies. Two relatives of Mbaliki died and we gave him two days off for each of the funerals. Mr. Mlinga, the handicraft teacher, lost his baby son and we all marched four miles down to the Catholic cemetery to bury him.

Of course it wasn't really the cold that killed them. We'd be sick ourselves, these days, vicious stomach pains that seemed to slice through your middle. No doubt something from the water. The pains would usually begin in the evening, so sudden and searing that if you were close to the house you'd just have time to make it to the *choo*. But if you weren't near, out walking maybe, then you'd just have time to reach the bushes and drop your pants, hoping that no one passing would see you.

We'd hear the drums every evening now. Sometimes they played because of a funeral, other times it was just a *ngoma* or dance. Those drums, I remember the chill they had sent through me, hearing them that first night at Martin Martinson's, or late at night, coming from across the valley. Jungle drums in the darkest Africa. I guess that's one of the images you come to Africa with—of drums and natives dancing frenetically around the fire, a human sacrifice boiling in the pot. Or the jungle drums beating out their message of warning—a lion loose or an approaching war party.

Well, here the drums were in our own back yard so to speak. Or in Swahili, *ng'ambo,* which means across the river. They would echo for miles and you would begin following the *boom, boom, boom,* the *thump, thump, thump*—it seemed so near—down little paths, up the back of a mountain and down the front, across a stream at the bottom and then back up another mountain.

Until you came to the spot, a clearing with five or six huts around the outside. With maybe twenty or thirty Africans, old men, young men, even some boys, dressed in their torn shirts and torn shorts, some in trousers, some even wearing shoes, bobbing and weaving, reeling from their pombe, staggering in a long line that bedraggled into a circle. The drum pounding, each dancer holding a gourd in his right hand into which he blew, sounding like a kazoo, chanting a howl at the top of his lungs, *Aaaoo, AAAuu.*

Old men, very old men, sitting on the side, would welcome us very warmly, shaking our hands with a warm *Oogonile, ndaga,* bringing us chairs for us to sit next to them—a privilege to sit next to the elders. And we would watch the dancers, fascinated, the old men nodding and smiling to each other, offering us bowls of pombe.

Now, old women, each with a black cloth wrapped about her middle, running through the lines of the dancers, whistling a shrill piercing sound with her tongue against her teeth. While the dancers, holding a leaf or a cloth in their hands, would bend and bow and sway to each other with exaggerated motions, now to the ground, to the sky—perhaps the same motions of centuries ago— with a significance perhaps of how many hundreds of years?

But the chilling sound of drums in the night didn't signify a human sacrifice roasting in the pot, or a wild animal they were about to hunt, or an approaching war party. Instead, these cannibals, these flesh eaters, were a group of half-dressed natives, half drunk on their pombe, celebrating an afternoon the way we would take in a ball game or shoot a round of golf.

·     ·     ·

We were doing circles now in math. I brought in ten pots and jars of different sizes, and the boys measured the radius and diameter, and then the circumference by tying a string around each one. We drew our findings on the board in a little chart so that we could note the relationship between radius and diameter and circumference. And it was easy to see that the diameter was twice the radius, but what about the circumference? That didn't quite seem to come out the same.

Then Fedson Mwandemele said that it looked as though the circumference was about three times the diameter, No, he said, correcting himself, it is three times but a little more.

Yes, that's right, I said, that's just what it is, and I explained that the circumference is a little more than three times the diameter, about 3.14, but that no one ever found the exact number, and that we called this number pi, $\pi$.

Then someone raised his hand and said that he had seen pi written as 22/7. Hmm, I said, not explaining, looking very mysterious, what do you think about that, boys? Does this mean that pi is 22/7 and not 3.14?

They didn't say anything for a while, just sitting there with that puzzled look about them. Had I told them the wrong thing?

Then Fedson said, Yes, I think 22/7 is correct, they are both correct, because you said that no one had ever found the exact number, and 22/7 is almost the same as 3.14.

Exactly, I said, that's exactly right, and I divided 22/7 on the board and of course it came out 3.14 with something left over, and their eyes lit up. See, I said to them, it's just about the same, 22/7 or 3.14. Not exactly, because of the little remainder, and I pointed to it again, but close enough.

All right, I said, now if the radius is 120, what is the diameter? They all had their hands up, that was easy enough, they all knew it was 240. And then what would the circumference be, using 3.14 as pi?

And they all knew that just as quick, correct, they would just multiply the diameter by 3.14.

So I showed them the formulas $\pi d$ and $2 \pi r$ so they'd see what they looked like, and then I said, Now let's say you have the circumference, how would you find the radius? And again they all had their hands up, quick without thinking.

Yes, I said, calling on someone who I was sure would get it, we would divide by 3.14—what would that give you? Diameter, they answered in chorus. And for radius—and again in chorus, Divide by two. And it wasn't that this was some great concept, it was just the ease with which they grasped something when it was explained clearly to them.

We went through it again as there were usually five or ten of them who didn't catch it the first time. Then I told them to take out their notebooks, we were having a test, and quickly I wrote five radii on the board and told them to find diameter and circumference, and then five circumferences, telling them to find diameter and radius. But I only gave them fifteen minutes, which really is plenty of time for Standard 7, except that these kids were so poor with their fundamentals and so slow that many of them wouldn't finish.

Now while I was collecting the papers, those that hadn't finished would be scribbling furiously until the last possible second, and by the time I reached the front of the room with all the papers, they would already have their hands raised. Did I think it might be possible to give them another test tomorrow as they were afraid they hadn't done well today? They hadn't a chance to finish, they had worked too slowly. Would it be possible to give them some extra sums tonight just for practice?

And that's how they were, these kids. Bright, yes, I was beginning to discover, and so, so eager. Could they have another test tomorrow, or more sums? You bet they could, they could have a test every day and extra sums every night if it would help them. How could you beat kids like that?

In science we were doing a chapter on the earth, the sun, and the planets. What is a day, what is a year? That morning I took them outside, and we pointed to where the sun was, just above the dormitories. Then I collected them at lunchtime and we saw that the sun was directly overhead. And again after supper as it was settling behind the blue mountains.

Next day in class I said to them, You know, boys, it looks as though the sun is moving, doesn't it? Remember where it was in the morning and where it was after supper? How did it get from the dormitories over to the mountains? Well, let's see what really happens. I called one big boy, Daudi Kipopwe, to the front of the room, and a little one, Betson Nsanya. Daudi will be the sun, I said, and Betson the earth. Now let's see what will happen, and I told Daudi to stand still and told Betson to walk around him, making a full circle around the sun, and coming back to the place where he had begun, rotating his body as he turned.

All right, boys, I said. Let's notice what has happened. Isn't Daudi, in the middle, bigger than Betson, who is going around him? Well, Daudi is the sun and Betson is the earth, and we can see that the sun—Daudi—is bigger than the earth—Betson—and that the earth—Betson—moves or revolves around the sun—Daudi. That it is the earth that moves, not the sun.

Now, I said, watch Betson as he revolves, and I pushed him off. See how his body is turning as he revolves. His body is rotating— and I said the word *rotating* very slowly, to make sure they heard the difference between *rotate* and *revolve*. This is what the earth does. As it revolves in a kind of circle around the sun, it is also rotating, turning itself on its axis.

Now let us say that Betson's face is Africa and that his back is America. Look now how Betson is facing Daudi, Africa is facing the sun. That means that it is day here in Africa. But look at Betson's back, America. It is away from the sun. America is away from the sun. That means it is night in America. So that when it is day in Africa, it is night in America.

92

Then someone asked, Does that mean that when Betson's back is toward the sun, it is night in Africa and day in America?

Exactly. That's just what it means. When it is day in Africa like right now, it is night in America. And when it is night in Africa, it is day in America.

But now some more hands were up. Do you mean that right now, right now, it is night in America?

Exactly, I said. Now, this minute, while we are in this classroom, people in America are sleeping in their beds, and they looked at each other, laughing and shaking their heads.

By the way, I said to them, what do we call it when Betson rotates his body one complete time? What does it mean when he has made a complete rotation? How long does it take?

Ahh, they said. Twenty-four hours. One day.

So that one rotation is twenty-four hours. Good.

Now I said to them, How long do you think it will take Betson to make one revolution, making sure to say the word revolution very slowly so that they could hear the difference again between revolution and rotation. How long will it take Betson to revolve once around the sun and to come back to the same spot on the floor? What will we call it when Betson has returned to the same spot on the floor where he began?

Ahh, they said, as the light dawned. One year. And they nodded to each other. One year.

Which is how many days, how many rotations? And I said the word very slowly again.

Three hundred and sixty-five days, they said. That is one year. Solved.

Classes were punctuated with regularly spaced staff meetings. They were in Swahili now—we were beginning to pick up enough of the language to make ourselves hesitatingly understood, although we rarely could catch all that they were saying—and with the shedding of English the teachers metamorphosed from calm gentle friends into fierce savages, accusing each other, arguing and screaming with all the fury of a little war.

The Twak would usually begin by announcing that they had disgraced the profession of teaching, that they were spending all their time drinking at Ushirika, not teaching when they were supposed to. For what he had done was to devise the latest schedule for the

Standard 8 boys, according to which they were to have classes through the afternoon and at night. Which meant that all of us would be teaching an extra two or three periods a week.

And at first all the teachers agreed to go along with it. For the Twak had said to them, as he unveiled his plan, Is there anyone who does not want to help these boys? And of course no one wanted to say yes to that. But when the schedule went into effect the teachers just continued going to Ushirika every afternoon at four-thirty the way they always did, whether they were supposed to be teaching or not.

Now the Twak was accusing them. And they would sit there with hands folded in front of them, looking down at the floor like penitent schoolboys. He would say, But perhaps you do not want to help these boys, and they would look up offended as if to say, How can you say that about us? Of course we want to help them, we do, we do. And they would solemnly agree to follow the timetable diligently this time, never to go to Ushirika when it was their turn to teach in the afternoon or at night.

And they would follow the schedule—for a few days, maybe even for a week. But then they would start all over again, skipping a period, then another, and soon all of them were back to Ushirika just as before.

And the same thing would go on at the next meeting, the Twak accusing them, all of them sitting there as penitently as before, all solemnly agreeing to uphold the new schedule, down to the last period of recorded time. No, they wouldn't be going to Ushirika any more, it wouldn't happen again. Until the next time.

Sometimes the Twak would accuse teachers individually. Mr. Mlinga had been talking to the villagers about school matters. Didn't they understand that these school affairs were private and confidential? A good teacher didn't even discuss such things with his wife—as though these staff meetings were of international importance. Or Mr. Mwadunda might accuse Mr. Mwaisunga of not paying for his bowl of pombe last week, or Mr. Mwambigila had been saying bad words about Mr. Ngulu, as the Twak nodded his head, Very, very, very bad indeed. Didn't they realize that they the teachers had a position of dignity to uphold here in the village?

And that would usually bring him around to Mr. Ngubile, who, he heard, was ordering some schoolgirls to do work for him in his house and then seducing them. It was very serious—he wagged his long black mustache—very, very, *mbaya sana,* Mr. Ngubile. Mr. Ngubile sat staring at the floor, never saying a word. Was he above defending himself or was he merely acquiescing?

Then the Twak would say that he had something very important to discuss. Which always meant that he was going to say something about Mr. Biboko. That he had been drunk again at Ushirika, insulting the Nyakusa tribe. Or frightening the boys with his Tanga magic.

And that would send the Twak off into the long harangue about the famed cracked-teacup incident, the teachers all nodding their heads wisely and knowingly, Yes, they had all heard about it. With Mr. Biboko sitting there just looking at the ground as Mr. Ngubile had. And after the meeting, coming over to us, Mike and me, whispering confidentially, You see, my young *broos,* just as I have told you, these people fear me because of my intelligence.

We had one meeting when the Twak received a circular from the Chief Education Officer of the district, that teachers were beating students too much, it was against the Tanganyikan Educational Code, as drawn up by the Ministry for that year. Was it the beating or the beating too much that was against the Tanganyikan Educational Code, I wondered.

What we really needed, I said, was a reorganization of the whole method of punishing the boys, and the Twak nodded his head, Yes, yes, very very, that was exactly right. We should beat the boys only when there was absolutely no one around to see, he said.

Occasionally I tried to bring up something about the sports program. Maybe we could have a whole reorganization of that too. Yes, yes, very very, the Twak said. Except that the 8's were studying every afternoon and the other classes would be doing their work around the school. But we should try, he nodded, yes, very very.

.    .    .

Once a month we would try to get to Mbeya, Mike and I. Not that there was very much to do there, but at least we could get a hot shower and there was a golf course. It was even good seeing Kim Buck. But most important, it would just be a break from Ndumulu School, from those staff meetings and the Twak's harangues, from the endless succession of pombe bowls, from the assemblies when sometimes you thought you just weren't going to come out of your house when they started gonging the bell, or even from classes when you'd sometimes find yourself shouting at the kids when you meant to be explaining.

We would leave Ndumulu on Friday after our last period, walking to Ushirika, where we could catch the five o'clock bus to Mbeya. Where were we going? people along the road would call out to us, and the women who were inside their huts would stick their heads out to hear, or someone chopping wood would stop work and look at us as we spoke to someone else.

We were going to Mbeya, we would say, and they'd nod their heads, Ahh, Mbeya.

And for how long? Oh, just a couple of days.

To do what? Oh, just to visit. And they'd nod again.

When were we coming back? they wanted to know, and I always had this funny feeling that they didn't really believe we were coming back.

Sometimes Europeans from the tea plantations would be passing, and they would always pick us up. Or missionaries—there seemed to be a large contingent of them, Swiss Moravians, Catholic sisters and brothers, Lutherans, even an American couple, Baptists from Texas—and they would always stop for us, except that they always wanted to know if we wouldn't like to go to church with them on Sunday.

One Friday the Americans—Just call me Rod, he said to us, and this here's my wife Rolene—brought us to their home for supper. They lived near the Starks, with the same beautiful lawn and beautiful view, with two African servants and a giant deepfreeze that had been shipped over by their mission society back in America. And four little blond, blue-eyed children sat silently on the floor playing Monopoly as one of the Africans served them cookies and lemonade.

Just before dinner they gave us a little music hour. One of the blond children played the violin while Rod accompanied on the piano and Rolene led the rest in singing hymns.

For supper we had hippo meat. Rod had been hunting with some other missionaries just the week before, he said, and it sounded as though they had shot up a whole herd of them. They had filled the deepfreeze with all the hippo they had shot, which gives you some idea of the size of the deepfreeze. Actually, though, the hippo was very good. A cross between a well-done steak and pot roast, I would say.

After dinner Rod led Mike and me around the garage, where he said he had something special to show us—into a little room he had constructed, with a little shortwave set he had rigged up. He turned it on and lo, it was Mel Allen, the White Sox and the Yankees, right from the Stadium—must be a day game—Tony Kubek leading off the bottom of the first and How about that, folks!

There were also some Catholics, brothers, who lived together in a mission station just outside Tukuyu, each of them with one small room, only a bed, and a crucifix on the wall. One was especially nice, a young fellow, not too much older than we were, Brother Pierre who came from Montreal. He had only been here four months, he said, and he was planning to spend his whole life out here working with the African people.

And I couldn't help thinking of Ndumulu School, of the Africans, how they all went to church every Sunday, all the boys and all the villagers, all with their different sects, all to the same church, all dressed in the brightest, newest clothes, singing the hymns in Kinyakusa.

I also thought about a composition I had assigned the boys, What they wanted to accomplish in the future, and how most of them had written about having a house, a car, many children, and many wives. Many wives. All these boys who were Christians, who went to church and sang hymns every Sunday. And Mr. Ngubile with his two wives. He was the one who sang the loudest.

And I couldn't help feeling sorry for Brother Pierre, there in his bare room. He was giving his life, but what results would he achieve? Were they Christians because they went to church on Sundays and sang their hymns? Is that what being a Christian means?

Well, maybe Brother Pierre would really change them. Maybe he was different. Certainly he was different from Rod and Rolene. Somehow it was hard to feel sorry for them, they had it too good for you to feel sorry for them.

Usually though there were no Europeans at Ushirika, and we would stand there in front of Daniel Mwamatuma's waiting for the bus while people would be shouting, *Broo, broo,* rushing over and slapping palms, so happy to see us. Except that you had to be careful about being a little too friendly because many of them were also going to Mbeya, and in case a European from the tea plantation did come, you'd feel awfully stupid getting into the car, the driver saying to the Africans standing around us—as they never would take Africans in their cars—Sorry, no room for you, with a whole empty back seat staring at them.

Then a faint noise in the distance, a cloud of dust rising, and you could see the bus now, old and sagging, with peeling yellow paint as it chugged and sputtered forward, panting to a stop as it reached us. A swarm of half-naked little boys carrying handfuls of food would surround it, yelling inside at the passengers through the windows, *Mayai, machungwa, mandazi, ndizi*—Swahili for eggs, oranges, rolls, bananas—in the tone of old-time newsboys on the corner crying, Extra, extra, read all about it, get your afternoon paper only five cents.

A group of women would pile out of the bus, each one pointing to the luggage rack on top. And the conductor would climb up there, each woman directing him to the bundle she wanted. Then they would bring some other bundle out of the bus—fresh fish or a live chicken—which they couldn't have placed on top, while the people from Ushirika would be entering the same door to make sure that they got a seat by a window.

Inside it was hot and sweaty, two or three to a seat, with babies crying on their mothers' backs or sucking at their breasts, and everyone crowded together so that you couldn't turn around. And outside the half-naked little children shouting, *Mayai, machungwa, mandazi, ndizi,* the people sticking their hands out the window with pieces of change in them, taking some *mayai* or *machungwa* from the hands of the little boys, and starting to eat the eggs and bananas, throwing the peels and the shells all over the floor. And many women with their bundles of fresh fish with them, chickens with their legs tied squawking, defecating on the floor. And the flies, the buzzing and the smell, the smell.

Then everything would seem ready, only the driver would still be inside one of the shops drinking a cup of tea or sipping a bowl of pombe. But finally he would come, and the bus would begin, the little boys selling the food scattering like flies as the bus bumped slowly off.

It would be unable to go more than five or ten miles an hour up the hills, but making good time on the straightaway and downhill, except that every time we seemed to get up a good speed, someone would begin pounding on the window or yelling to the driver, Stop, he wanted to get off.

So the bus would chug to a stop, the person would get out, the conductor climbing to the top to get his load. Then we were ready, but someone would see something he wanted to buy—a chicken maybe or a fish that was drying in the sun. So he'd ask the driver if he would wait just a minute and he would jump out, while some other people would also jump out, one to greet a friend he had just seen passing, another to urinate along the side of the road. And then a new person would be running up from somewhere out of the bushes, bringing his own bundle and his own smell.

We'd get to a town and another group of half-naked little boys would surround the bus, shrieking *Mayai, machungwa, mandazi, ndizi,* the passengers sticking their hands out the window, peeling the food on the floor. One time a man tried to leave without paying as the bus began to pull away, the little boy running after it, howling for the penny for his *machungwa.* And everyone inside the bus turned on this man shouting at him, *Mwizi, mwizi,* thief, thief, stealing from a little child. So finally before we'd gone too far, he threw the money out the window for the little boy who was still running behind, chasing the bus, as they all laughed to each other and slapped palms, nodding their heads and laughing at the man, and he laughed too.

Sometimes we would ride with Wasafua, who are a tribe halfway between Tukuyu and Mbeya, more dirty than the usual, with scars on their faces and breasts hanging down, wearing only thin strips across their midsections. They had their own peculiar kind of smell, which came, no doubt, from weeks or even months of not washing.

And we would pass buses overturned, cars abandoned, trucks with flat tires. Usually the same cars would be there on Sunday when we returned. Occasionally we'd break down ourselves and the driver would step out and fumble about under the hood for a while or get some assistance from a passing bus. But sometimes fumbling did no good or there were no passing buses, and the driver would announce that we had broken down, *kabisa,* and that there wasn't another bus due until the next morning.

That meant we would have to sleep there in the bus. And the

thing is, they would just accept it, these people, without the slightest bit of grumbling or complaining, just *ndiyo, bwana, ndiyo,* nodding their heads and starting to take out their bowls of food as night was coming on, while Mike and I would climb out, hoping to flag down somebody, maybe there was someone going through, as the rest of them took out their blankets for the night.

So it would never be before midnight that we got in—if then. We would sleep at Kim Buck's house, his wife would make some special dish for us, and we would sit around playing poker with Kim and some of the others who might have come in. And Kim Buck would tell us what a fine job we were doing there, Mike and I, how he always heard people talking about how friendly and cooperative we were, how they all liked us so much down there, that in fact they were sending someone from Washington out, and bringing him down there to Ndumulu just to see us. How the hell had we broken the projector, though?

. . .

One day Mr. Mapunda drove to Ndumulu to announce that the Minister of something like Cooperatives and Finance was coming to Tukuyu tomorrow. Mr. Mapunda was the local TANU officer. He said that the Minister was flying from Dar es Salaam—which is the capital—and that he would land on the airfield, which one of the nearby tea companies owned. And that TANU had decided all the schoolboys of the area should be there to greet the Minister when he landed, only they weren't sure just what time he was coming, so they wanted us all to be there at eight in the morning in case he came early.

We held a staff meeting and Mr. Twakatulu said that we must leave no later than seven, which meant that the boys would have to get up before six. But something went wrong and we didn't leave until after eight, the band booming and squeaking through the brick arch, the white shirts now covering the road, and people from inside their huts hearing the noise, peeking out and beginning to follow.

Soon we turned into another road, and it was filled with people, all going toward the landing field, more schools with their bands, old men in torn sheets, old women in bright *kongas,* cars passing with government officials from Tukuyu. And now two big open trucks filled with people standing in the back, as though they had all been collected and packed there in the back of the truck, one on top of the other like dried fish. And they were all singing the TANU song, *Ooho TANU, yajenga nchi, Ooho TANU, yajenga nchi.*

Then at the landing field—really nothing more than a strip of grass, not much longer than a football field—more people, the government officials, stepping out of their cars—they were young men, wearing tapered trousers and pointed black Italian shoes—women with the babies around their necks—the schoolboys, marching up and back across the field—other villagers on the sidelines, waving and smiling to their friends. And now dancers with gourds, bowing and bending between the rows of schoolboys, looking up at the sky for a sign of the plane, a fleck of silver in the blue sky.

But there was no fleck of silver—only the blue sky. It grew later and later, the sun growing hotter and hotter, the schoolboys still marching up and back with the dancers gyrating in and out, government officials standing in front of their cars, the villagers on the sidelines still calling and waving to their friends.

Mr. Ngubile came up to me and said that the teachers were all going off to drink pombe, as someone had just come from Tukuyu and had told him that the Minister wasn't coming until tomorrow. Soon the rumor began floating through the crowd—everyone was buzzing about it—someone had just come from Tukuyu. There had been a misunderstanding somewhere, the Minister wasn't coming until tomorrow.

So Mr. Mapunda collected some of the villagers into a group, and they began to sing the TANU song, *Ooho TANU, yajenga nchi, Ooho TANU, yajenga nchi.* And then they were all singing, all the villagers, all the schoolboys, as the government officials stepped back into their cars, as the villagers climbed into the backs of the trucks, as the schoolboys drifted into their formations, drums booming, flutes squeaking, as we headed back to school.

And there were the teachers, fitting themselves into line, Mr. Ngubile saying, See, what did I tell you, *broo,* slapping palms and laughing, passing other villagers who were smiling and waving. No matter, they would come tomorrow, as though they didn't even care that they had walked five or maybe more miles, that they had wasted the whole day.

Next morning we set out again, through the brick arch, the same booms and squeaks, the same villagers turning out of their huts to follow, passing the same other schools and their bands, the same cars of the government officials, the same two open trucks with their loads of passengers, still singing *Ooho TANU, yajenga nchi.*

There at the landing strip, waiting and waiting, the sun growing hotter and hotter, the boys marching up and back, the dancers with their gourds, the villagers smiling and waving on the side, with Mr. Ngubile coming over to me, they were going off again to pombelize, they didn't think the Minster would be there for a while.

Then someone pointed to the sky, and all the heads looked up. There it was, a silver speck in the blue. Growing larger and larger, circling the field now. A Piper Cub.

And now the TANU officials shooing them all off to the sidelines, the villagers staring at the plane as it approached the runway —I wondered for how many it was the first time they had ever seen a plane—as Mr. Mapunda tried to start them singing *Ooho TANU,* but they were too busy staring.

It came to a halt, the door opened and out popped a European, the pilot. And from the other door a fat little black man with an oversized sport shirt, stepping carefully out of the plane and walking very deliberately, as all the government officials and TANU people raced over to him to embrace him. He was standing there, looking at them very seriously and very solemnly as they raised their arms and shouted *Uhuru* to each other, to the crowd.

*Uhuru,* as the crowd all lifted their arms, *Uhuru.*

Now they led him through the lines of people, Mr. Mapunda introducing him to the local officials. He walking very slowly, his face expressionless and vacant, nodding his head briefly to one, haughtily to another, as though he were almost bored by it all. Two days of waiting for him and a nod like that.

Then he was through the lines and into the TANU car, the young government officers racing into their cars behind him, they were all going to Tukuyu.

So they rounded up the boys into their formations and they began marching back to school. The older people began singing, climbing back into those two big open trucks. Two days of waiting and then off like this, after five minutes!

And I couldn't help thinking of that first day we had come to Ndumulu, the preparations they had made for the tea party, how they had waited for us since the morning, and how we had done just the same thing as the Minister, running off that way to Martin Martinson's. How many times before had that happened in their lives; how many times would it happen again?

. . .

We were supposed to go to Dar es Salaam for Saba Saba Day. Saba Saba Day commemorates the founding of TANU, and this year they had planned a giant celebration, bringing various teams and entertainers from all over the country to Dar.

We had finally built a basketball court, measuring out a good size and having about twenty boys level it with their *jembes,* hunting all over the area for planks of wood and running back and forth between the Twak and the Educational Officer in Tukuyu for the rims. Finally, though, we had had to write to Kim Buck to supply them, and he had shipped them from Mbeya a few days later.

The boys had taken right to the game. Every afternoon you could hear their squeals as they scrambled and flip-flopped over the ball, which rolled all over the court like a greased watermelon. They could go for hours on end, the same ten of them at a time, not even the volume of their squeals lessening as I'd run up and down the sidelines with the whistle, yelling, Walking, walking, or Pushing, pushing, or Slowly, boys, slowly.

One day the Twak happened to be passing by, and hearing all the commotion, he sauntered over. Taking one look at the boys falling all over each other as they fought for the ball, he suddenly ripped off his shoes and raced onto the court, screaming at the boy with the ball, Here, here, pass it here.

My first thought was that the Twak actually knew the game, so commanding was his voice. Of course the boy threw it to him. And the Twak started jumping up and down with excitement—without dribbling the ball, however, so I blew the whistle on him for walking. He looked at me as though he didn't understand what was happening, why couldn't he keep the ball? I explained the rule to him. Then he started yelling at the boy who had thrown him the ball.

By this time the other team had lost it, so the Twak's team had it again, the Twak screaming, Here, here, pass it here. And he began jumping up and down as they threw it to him again, just as he had done before. Then, hearing my whistle, he looked up at me with the most pained expression on his face, as the whole sequence would begin again.

We even made up a team, Mike and I, fifteen of them. Mike had chosen only little boys, who, he said, never had a chance to play soccer because they were too small. That was Mike's way.

One day the Twak asked me confidentially why it was that there were only little boys on the team. And for some reason that I can't really explain very well, I just didn't want to tell him, so I said that we used the little ones because their bodies were closer to the ground. It would be more difficult to take the ball away from them as it had a shorter distance to travel from the ground to their hands when they dribbled. And I reminded him how the ball was always rolling all over the court, he nodding his head vehemently to show that he understood this scientific principle.

About a week later the Twak asked me how the boys were doing. He hadn't been able to play himself, he explained, as he had been quite busy in Tukuyu over the Saba Saba Day preparations. Then he asked me, Did I think Ndumulu could defeat all the other schools in the district? And I said, Yes, I thought we could, because Mike and I would be playing and no one else knew how to play the game. Only I didn't say it quite that way.

About a week later he asked me how I thought our team would do if we went to Dar es Salaam, because he had mentioned it to the local TANU people how we had chosen the shortest boys so that they would be closer to the ground. And they had seemed very impressed, they had suggested that we should take the basketball team to Dar es Salaam as the regional team. If that was all right with me.

Was it all right with me! I almost jumped out of my clothes. A week in Dar es Salaam. The beach. Fresh lobster! A real holiday! Was it all right with me! Whatever brand of basketball they played in Dar es Salaam, it couldn't be too strong—at least nothing that a week on the beach or some good lobster couldn't handle.

Only what about school, I said. Wouldn't we be going in the middle of classes? They must have forgotten about that.

No matter, he said, shaking his head. This is more important. It is for *Yajenga nchi* building the nation.

So we got ourselves ready, Mike and I. A week in Dar es Salaam —who were we to argue with building the nation? Each night we talked about what we would do first, how we would lie there in the sun on the white beaches, with the blue water and the palm trees.

I knew none of the boys had been to Dar es Salaam. How nice it would be to take them to dinner at a good restaurant there, with clean white tablecloths, with music, with waiters in dark uniforms. How wonderful it would be for them. When again would they get an opportunity like this? I'd even pick up the tab myself.

So I told them how hard we would have to work in the next three weeks to get ourselves ready. I even thought of making some taller additions to the squad, but I figured it might destroy the Twak's faith in us. So we just stuck with what we had, watching them tear up and down the court, day after day, only we wouldn't let them squeal any more—it was business now—we were going to Dar es Salaam.

We'd go from four until it was dark, every day now, with one hour for fundamentals, dribbling and passing, another for scrimmaging. We even tried teaching them a 1 2 2 zone, but I figured that was only asking for trouble, so we just stuck to our sort of floating man to man, with Mike and me, the deep men, to keep an eye on anything serious.

And maybe it was my imagination, but they didn't seem to be bumping into each other as much. And we began marking the days off, the Twak said we would be leaving on Saturday, that the football team would be playing that day in Tukuyu for the Saba Saba Day cup, so the whole school would be going to Tukuyu that day. After the game they would all see us off, the TANU people had our tickets and we would leave on the five o'clock bus.

Well, that was what we were supposed to do. We came to Tukuyu with our bags packed, marching up and down with the band. I was feeling so good I bought myself a black tuxedo coat for fifteen shillings from one of the wandering Arabs in long, colorful robes who rode around on bicycles. People greeted us, *Oogonile, ndaga,* smiling and asking me about my coat, where did I get it, feeling it, taking it off to show someone, then seeing the label, Lippincott, San Francisco.

My God, maybe it was a CARE package. So this is where they were sent, Tukuyu, Tanganyika, the end of the road.

And while we are marching, with all the noise of the bands, waving and *Oogonile*-ing to people on the side, the Twak comes up to us and says something about a cancellation, there has been a change of plans, they want us to stay in Tukuyu and hold the basketball tournament here instead of in Dar es Salaam. And I just stare at him. What's that? I can't have heard him right with all the noise.

He tells us again, and I hear myself saying, You mean we're not going at all? The whole thing has been canceled? And he nods his head.

You mean we're not going, not even for a day? Not at all? And suddenly I realize I must be sounding like poor Macduff, hearing about his children, All my pretty ones? Did you say all? All?

I looked back to the Twak, but he had run off someplace, I could hear him yelling now at one of the boys who was out of line. So I just stood there with all the noise around me, what was there to do? Mr. Twakatulu couldn't have realized how much we had wanted to go, he couldn't have if he had told us like this, so abruptly, so offhandedly, that there was no trip to Dar es Salaam. Only the booming of the drums, the tooting and squeaking of the flutes. And what could you do but continue marching in line with everyone else, just letting yourself be pushed along?

We were going toward the soccer field now, our boys were already out there on the field, wearing old shabby uniforms they had just been given—with holes in them. With the Twak standing nearby, I could hear him arguing with someone; it seemed they all wanted him to play in this game because he had once been a championship player, but he was saying, No, that he was too old, he only coached nowadays.

I looked down on the field again, the boys were passing, kicking the ball around to each other, and they were going to their positions now, the game was beginning. And suddenly there was the Twak running out there, he was pulling off his shoes and his shirt, and one of the boys was taking off his uniform and giving it to him, the crowd roaring, and the boy walking off the field, the game beginning.

And the Twak was everywhere, blocking the ball, passing, kicking, the crowd howling at everything he did. Everyone was watching the Twak, and the game out there; no one cared that we weren't going to Dar es Salaam.

I saw some of the members of our basketball team, the little boys, standing with their bags, jumping up and down, cheering. I

106

guessed they hadn't heard they weren't going. It seemed so unfair to them, they were so happy, they were looking forward to it as much as we were. Someone would have to tell them though; it might as well be us.

So I said, I have some bad news, boys, and they said, Yes, we know, we aren't going to Dar es Salaam, as they turned back to the game. The Twak in alone on the goalie, a shot, a goal, and a great roar as these little boys jumped up and down and hugged each other.

You mean you have heard? I asked them again.

Yes, they said, looking at me. But now the game had started again, their eyes, their heads were back on the field, they weren't upset at all about it, they didn't seem to care. We were the only ones who cared.

And suddenly I wanted to get out of there, away from the field, away from all these happy people. Come on, I said to Mike, nobody will miss us, and we headed to the road for school.

Soon a car passed us and stopped. Europeans. And a hearty voice said, Why don't you come over to the house for a cup of tea? It was the Starks.

I dropped myself into the car. It had been a long time since they had seen us, they said—not since the day when they had taken us with them to the club—more than six months ago. Was it six months, I thought. How much had happened in that time.

Then suddenly, I don't even know why, it was the strangest thing, I just started to babble about what had happened to us, how we had been planning to go to Dar es Salaam, how we had practiced for three weeks, how we had all come today with our bags packed, and how it had all been canceled, so suddenly, so abruptly, how the Twak had told us, how neither he nor anyone else seemed to care. At least if he had said, I'm sorry, I know how hard you've worked—but no, three weeks of planning just melted away with one sentence from him.

And that's the way things are done around here, the way all the hopes and plans can disintegrate with just a word, and worse still nobody even seems to care. I could feel my voice getting funny as though it were about to crack, it was the oddest thing, what was the matter with me?

And suddenly I realized that it wasn't only Dar es Salaam that I was talking about and feeling so hurt about, it was everything all together—all the long waits, the staff meetings, the confusions, the sports program we had tried to arrange, everything that we had come here to do, and this was the way it was all turning out.

They didn't say anything as I spoke, they just let me go on to get it all out of my system. When we got to the house they brought the tea—Ernest—and Mrs. Stark went and turned on the bath. That was nice of her. She began talking to us, telling us some stories about Africans, things they themselves were both familiar with as they had been there for so long, and which we would soon be used to the longer we lived there.

She told us about an old African who had become a Minister when his country had obtained independence, really a very nice old fellow, she said, but completely illiterate. And after a hard day's work he liked nothing better than to go home to his mud hut, which he had built in back of his government house, take off his shoes and clothes, put on his long tribal robes and sit on the floor drinking his pombe.

Then she asked, How is Mbaliki—to cheer me up, no doubt. I told her how well he was working out, how he would stand there in my white tennis sneakers and his long black lady's overcoat, and we all laughed. And they brought us some cookies, they were so good, warm, and the tea was hot, and I was beginning to feel better. And the bath, letting myself down into the hot water, the steam rising, lying there with all my anger and hurt and disappointment soaking out through my pores into the hot water.

It was growing dark when we left. The Starks had offered to take us back to Ndumulu but we said no, everything was O.K. now, just sitting there, having someone listening to me had made it all right.

Soon a bus passed and we waved it down. The driver seemed very cheerful as we climbed in. How's Ndumulu? he asked. He had met us in Mbeya one day last month. Didn't we remember him?

Of course we did. It was just that we had done a lot of marching today and were very tired, and he nodded his head understandingly.

We chugged off, it was nearly night now, ahead was Ushirika. And the driver would not let us pay anything when we got out, we were his friends, it was all right. Also, he said, it was his way of thanking us for having come here to help Tanganyika. It's things like that that keep you going.

Mr. Ngubile and Mr. Biboko grabbed us as we stepped off the

bus, pulling us into Daniel Mwamatuma's. They had been there all afternoon, celebrating Saba Saba Day, they said, with a giant Saba Saba bowl of pombe. Inside were the rest of the teachers, they all jumped up when they saw us, bringing us two chairs, the muddy foamy bowl sitting there awaiting us in the middle of the table.

I drank deeply, letting it roll into my throat. I was tired. Better watch it or I would be drunk. Well, it didn't matter, I deserved it tonight after today.

The bowl went around, villagers stopping by the door to look at us as we waved to them. Then in staggered Mr. Mwadunda. He looked hard at us for a minute, and then he suddenly seemed to comprehend who we were, and he broke into a big smile, babbling and throwing his arms around his two new *broos*. Now he could tell us—how afraid they all had been before we came, how they had all wondered what kind of people we were, whether we would be very formal like the British, very reserved and standoffish and not laugh or drink with them.

But that really we were just the right kind of people to have come here. How we liked the same things as they did, we would always do everything together. And all the others sitting there nodding their heads and smiling.

I said something about how we were all *broos,* and we all slapped palms. My God, I was drunk.

Daniel Mwamatuma came in with a plate of *ugali.* We began to eat, all of us together from the bowl in the middle of the table. And Agnes stumbled in, weaving about, and sat down heavily, staring at us, with one of her breasts dangling outside her dress, as other villagers by the door staggered to our table and we passed the bowl to them.

Someone turned on the radio. It was a soccer game, coming from Dar es Salaam, the beginning of the Saba Saba Day festival, between an English team from Manchester and a Tanganyikan team, with an English announcer who would alternate with the Swahili announcer. I thought of Dar es Salaam and how much I would have liked to be there, at the beach, eating lobster, maybe at the stadium tonight. But instead we were back here in Ushirika, which is the farthest place in the country from Dar es Salaam, nearly five hundred miles away. Sitting here in Mwamatuma's hut, eating *ugali.*

I wondered if the others, the other teachers, wanted to go to Dar es Salaam as much as we did. Dar es Salaam, a kind of magical ring to the name. Did they think of it as we did, the magical name of a place that was hopelessly out of reach? Did they want to be there tonight for the beginning of the festival? Was it as far away for these poor villagers in their thatched-roof huts as it was for us? And as we sat there together, I felt, strangely enough, that we were really sharing something with these people, a longing perhaps, yes, that was it, sharing a longing, or was it just that I had drunk too much pombe?

· · ·

One Friday the bus we were on for Mbeya broke down just outside Tukuyu. It wasn't very late, just beginning to grow dark, so we started walking into town, Mike and I. Maybe we would meet some Europeans at their club and they would drive us back to Ndumulu that night. We could get the nine-o'clock bus tomorrow morning.

Suddenly a car pulled up and two Africans jumped out. Young men, wearing tapered trousers and pointed, black Italian shoes. Those officers that we had seen that day when the Minister had come. They shook hands and spoke to us in English. They had heard about us at Ndumulu and had seen us many times in Tukuyu, and that day at the airstrip. Yes, we nodded.

What were we doing here? they wanted to know.

So we told them about the bus, and they said, Would we like to come with them now, they were going to meet some of their friends, we could spend the night at their house in Tukuyu and catch the bus tomorrow morning.

So we said all right—we couldn't get a bus before morning anyway—and we fitted ourselves into the back seat of the car. There were two others inside and they introduced themselves. Moses, who was the district health inspector, and Simon, the agricultural officer. The first two were Hebron, who worked for community development, and Medson, the district treasurer.

They all spoke in English, very quickly and very fluently, with hardly a trace of an accent. I had never met anyone here who spoke English as well. They said they had each studied abroad for two years, Hebron and Moses in India, Medson in London, Simon in America.

We pulled into someone's house, and I noticed it was right next to the Starks'. A large house set back under some trees. But going up the driveway you could see thick grass and weeds sprouting up all over the lawn, and boxes of garbage lying outside on the back steps.

Medson apologized, it was his house. His wife had been away and had only returned last week, he said. Somehow that didn't quite explain the garbage on the back steps, or the grass that looked as though it hadn't been cut in months.

We followed them inside, into a big room that must have been the living room. Except that it was all bare, nothing in it at all but a torn, red-leather couch against the far wall. That whole room, no carpet, not a mat even, no pictures on the wall—only this torn red-leather couch.

A lady with short hair entered, wrapped in an orange *konga,* barefoot, holding a baby who was sucking at her breast. Medson said that this was his wife, and I thought I had been there long enough not to be surprised at most things, but I was surprised. Medson, who had studied abroad for two years. In London. And his wife no different from the wife of any villager.

Then a little girl came in, barefoot, wearing only a torn, soiled dress, like one of Mr. Biboko's little children or like any child we had grown accustomed to seeing. She carried a plate of meat and some hard-boiled eggs. Medson said this was his sister, who was staying with them, while he took out his pocketknife and cut some slices of meat, the others all reaching for the eggs, peeling them and throwing their shells on the floor. These officials who had all studied abroad. Throwing their shells on the floor like this. I wondered whether their wives were the same as Medson's. Did they have lawns with uncut grass and leave their garbage outside on the back steps?

After we had all finished they took us to another house, not far from Medson's. It was the home of Mr. Mapunda, the local TANU official, they said. There were many people there, more young men in Western clothes who spoke English to us, some old men wearing sheets and shoes with no laces, and two fat women in bright green dresses and green slippers who were running back and forth among the men, squeezing them and whispering into their ears while the men rubbed their thighs.

And there in the middle of the floor was a large black earthen bowl, with people drinking from it with wooden straws. On the top of the bowl was a kind of gray matter, which looked like ashes.

They would dip their straws down below the ashes and sip, bubbles rising on the surface as it passed up through their straws.

Pombe, they said to us, as they handed us straws.

But when we tried it our straws got all stuffed up until they showed us where to place them, just under the ashes near the sides of the bowl.

Now I sipped some, it was warm and sweet, something like applejack, it wasn't bad at all, actually quite good. They told us this was a Nyakusa drink called *kimpumu,* and I thought that it tasted better than any of the regular pombe we had been drinking.

Except now I noticed that when they finished drinking, they still had something left in their straws and they would spit it back into the bowl with the rest of the *kimpumu* that we were going to drink. I tried not to think about it too much, since it looked as though we were going to be drinking this for a long time, everybody seemed so contented just sitting there, drinking and talking to each other, these young officers sipping and spitting like the rest of them. And Moses a health officer.

And I thought of the story Mrs. Stark had told us, about the old African who had become a Minister, who would go home to his mud hut, take off his shoes, put on his robes and sit on the floor drinking a bowl of pombe. I could almost believe it now, seeing these young officers, these men who had all been abroad, who spoke English so well, who seemed as intelligent as anyone I had ever met, with their wives barefoot and bare-breasted, drinking the same pombe, and enjoying it as much as any villager. It was as though their Western dress and their English were nothing but a veneer, that really they weren't any different from any villager who had never even heard of London.

. . .

Then the roof fell in on Mr. Biboko. But not just Mr. Biboko, really it was on us too.

It had all started when he had come back drunk again to the dining hall one Saturday night, and had told the boys he was soon going to be headmaster and that Mr. Twakatulu was being sent away, that his Tanga magic was stronger than Mr. Twakatulu's Nyakusa magic. And Mike who was the duty teacher had gone to call Mr. Twakatulu, the way the Twak had told the duty teacher to do if Mr. Biboko ever started making trouble.

The Twak had come storming in, ordering Mr. Biboko to leave the dining room that instant. But Mr. Biboko had refused, and the Twak had stormed out, returning this time with some of the other teachers, while Mr. Biboko stood there calling them all names and insulting the Nyakusa tribe. Finally he had stumbled off to his house, where he had collapsed on the doorstep.

The Twak was furious, Mike had never seen him this way before, bouncing up and down, his teeth chattering, rolling his eyes and moaning over and over, Oh oh, this was the last time, the last time, they would have a meeting tomorrow, tomorrow, they would take steps this time, they would settle the matter once and for all.

Next morning the teachers gathered, talking about what they were going to say to Mr. Biboko at the meeting, bringing up all the old grievances that they had accumulated during the past year. All the insults and fights at Ushirika, Mr. Biboko and Mr. Mwadunda's wife, the famed cracked-teacup incident, which they related to each other again. And villagers began ambling over toward the office—I guess they had already heard the news of last night and wanted to see what would happen at the Great Meeting.

Then the teachers began heading over to the office as the villagers stood around in little groups. And there was the Twak, walking very briskly, looking straight ahead of him, with Mr. Biboko following a few paces behind, as though he were too afraid to speak to the Twak, or was it that the Twak was too angry to listen.

They were all in their seats when we came in, Mike and I, and the room suddenly became quiet. This was really important. As we sat down the Twak stood up, not saying anything, just bouncing up and down, his hands folded behind his back. He seemed especially nervous and I wondered just what he was going to say to Mr. Biboko.

He began talking now, looking down at the floor, saying that they were going to be speaking Swahili at this meeting, that they might be very angry. What was this? I thought. Weren't all their meetings in Swahili? Didn't they always get angry? What was he driving at?

Now he stopped talking, he just stood there in the front of the room. He was looking at us now, at Mike and me, not saying anything, just staring at us. Finally he blurted it out, It would be better if we weren't at this meeting.

Oh, I said. Such a little word that says so much.

They would be having another meeting tomorrow, he said as we stood up to leave. It would be a more important meeting. A sop.

The villagers were standing just outside the office, seeing us leaving, smiling to us, *Oogonile, ndaga,* Where were we going, quick, hurry, we shouldn't be late, it was a very important meeting.

And us trying to smile back at them.

They did have another meeting the next day just as the Twak had said. Only they didn't want us at that one either. And that afternoon the Twak came by to say that everything was all settled now, he was going to write to the Chief Educational Officer in Mbeya to ask him to have Mr. Biboko removed. Would I help him write the letter.

So I said All right—what else could I do? The letter was about how Mr. Biboko could no longer be tolerated by himself, Mr. Twakatulu, or the other teachers. And worse, by the boys. How could they respect him now after what he had done?

So I changed a word or two, a sentence here and there, and in a few days the Chief Educational Officer came and they all had another meeting—they didn't want us at this one either—and later after he had gone, the Twak came by again to tell us that Mr. Biboko was being transferred, and that there were going to be a lot of other transfers also, that's what the Chief Educational Officer had said, as he had heard stories about the teachers of Ndumulu drinking every day at Ushirika.

And in a few days an old broken-down truck appeared for Mr. Biboko, and they piled in his belongings, his beds, mattresses, cupboards, chairs, tables, and children all in the back of the truck, with his wife and babies in the front with him and the driver, while all the teachers stood around waving to him as the truck bumped through the brick arch, smiling and laughing just as though they had always been friends.

The night before they had all gone to his house to say goodbye, and they had spent the night drinking pombe, shouting and carrying on through the night. They had even come for us and we had gone and listened to the *babu* saying, My young *broos,* my young *broos,* and everybody slapping palms with everyone else, laughing together as though everything were the same as always.

And the thing was, to them everything was the same. Not just with Mr. Biboko but with us too—as though the fact that they

114

hadn't wanted us at those meetings hadn't meant anything to them at all. We were still as good friends as ever. At least if we had done something wrong, if we had made them angry, or if we had offended them . . . but no, we hadn't done anything at all, they just hadn't wanted us there. It was as simple as that.

And it was as though all the great friendships, all the handshaking at inspection, all the bowls of pombe we had drunk at Ushirika, all the times we had made some old man happy by saying *Oogonile,* all the words about being different from other white people, how we were just the kind of people they wanted—it just didn't mean anything at all. It was all a great sham, a great hoax. And the joke was on us, on Mike and me.

Not that they didn't mean what they said, not that Mr. Mwadunda hadn't meant it that night when he said how they had been afraid of us, but that we were just the kind of people they wanted, who shared things and laughed with them. No, I think he had meant it. But it was as though we were merely some kind of adornment to the staff of Ndumulu School, like a piece of jewelry worn around the neck, something to show to their friends. Look, we have an American teacher, isn't it nice how we all get along.

Marching with them all in Tukuyu, with everyone pointing to us, greeting us and smiling, how friendly we were, or going together to Mr. Ndendulu when his son had died. And now walking out the door with the villagers standing outside calling to us to return as quickly as we could, it was a very important meeting, we shouldn't miss it.

•   •   •

Just as the Twak had said, Mr. Biboko's departure was the beginning of a long line of departures. One by one other teachers received letters in the mail—that they were going to be transferred, that they should have their belongings ready, the truck was coming for them. And in a few days, or a week—you never could be sure exactly when—the old broken-down truck that had come for Mr. Biboko would appear, and that teacher would begin loading his furniture, his beds, mattresses, chairs and tables, and most of his children into the back of the truck, his wife and babies sitting in the cab.

They would ring the bell for the school to assemble, the boys standing stiffly in their lines, singing farewell songs, while the teacher climbed into the truck next to his wife, everyone waving goodbye as the truck rolled away through the brick arch.

In a few days the truck would appear again, with another teacher, a new one, with his wife and children, beds and mattresses, chairs and tables. They would ring the bell and the school would assemble, the boys singing songs of welcome as the new teacher climbed out.

Usually he knew one or two of the teachers from somewhere. They had taught together or they had been to the same teacher training college. Oh, *upo hapa,* are you here, he would say, and they would begin shaking hands and slapping palms like long-lost brothers.

Then the Twak would step forward and make a little speech, motioning for the new teacher to make a little speech also, as the boys applauded and sang more welcoming songs.

And in a few days another teacher would receive his letter, and the truck would appear again.

We lost four teachers after Mr. Biboko, and the funny thing was they didn't even seem to mind leaving, they would just accept it without a complaint and without a murmur, Mr. Mwambigila who was going to *mbu*—mosquito—country, or Mr. Mwadunda who was being transferred to the coast, after how many years here at Ndumulu. They would just shrug their shoulders—What can you do, *bwana?* One place is the same as another—and laugh to each other and slap palms.

Of course no one was teaching during these transfers. Everyone was too busy helping each teacher prepare for his journey, arranging his furniture, assisting him in getting his affairs in order, or returning the items he was responsible for, like the books of his classroom if he was the class master, or the knives and forks if he was in charge of the food store. And each new arrival and departure meant drawing up a new schedule, and then that would be changed in a few days because another teacher had received his letter. So the boys were told to sit in their classrooms and study on their own, the teachers had more important business to conduct.

In the middle of this, Mr. Kitandalala, the school inspector, appeared. He was going to be here for a week, to see every aspect of the school, from soup to nuts, he said. He had meant to come earlier this year—I remembered when the school had spent one week getting ready for him. Unfortunately he had had other pressing business, he said.

The Twak was beside himself. Somehow he felt that Mr. Kitandalala would hold him personally responsible for the fact that five teachers had been transferred in the last five weeks. He was running around, scribbling notes to all of us, We should be sure to go to classes each period, to leave off all other work, reminding us not to be late for anything, to be courteous and helpful at all times, to be well-dressed and maintain a good appearance, just what the manual of A Teacher's Duties and Responsibilities called for. And above all, warning the duty master under no circumstances to beat any boys—at least not where Mr. Kitandalala could see them being beaten.

He was a very British African, Mr. Kitandalala. He had been to London for a year, and he wore a Shetland sweater and a tweed coat, and he said his o's very openly—so, no, go—almost as if he were talking through his nose, and he smoked a pipe. He would sit in the class in the back of the room, his legs crossed, writing voluminous notes, as I explained about equilateral, right-angled and isosceles triangles, the boys bubbling over with questions and enthusiasm— Isn't an equilateral also isosceles? and Can't a right triangle be isosceles also?—just as I had taught them with squares and rectangles and quadrilaterals.

In English we were reading *Treasure Island* and I explained to them about Long John Silver and his wooden leg, what a pirate was, the kind of things he did, about the black spot, and their eyes widened and their mouths opened.

Then I had them read aloud:

> *Fifteen men on the dead man's chest*
> *Yo-ho-ho, and a bottle of rum!*

All together, loud, I said, pretending that you are a real pirate, and I said it for them the first time, mean and deep and gruff, just as a pirate would.

Then imitating me, deeply and gruffly, *Fifteen men on the dead man's chest,* shaking their heads to every beat, *Yo-ho-ho, and a bottle of rum,* as mean as they could. And then breaking out into big grins as they finished, they were so pleased with themselves.

One afternoon Mr. Kitandalala decided to inspect the dining hall during lunch. It was raining that day and the Twak, rather than let Mr. Kitandalala see the mud on the floor which the boys would track in from outside—because he wanted him to note how clean the dining hall was always kept—had ordered the boys to eat their lunch outside in the rain.

Seeing them standing there, holding their bowls waiting to be served, soaking wet in the pouring rain, Mr. Kitandalala said to the Twak, Why was it that the boys were standing outside in the rain? What was the matter with them, didn't they have sense enough to eat in the dining room under a dry roof when it rained?

And like a flash the Twak was leaping over at them and screaming, Why are you boys standing outside in the rain? What's the matter with you, don't you have enough sense to eat in the dining room under a dry roof when it is raining?

The day after Mr. Kitandalala left, the Great Ndumulu Scandal broke. It had begun innocently enough when I had happened to see two pupils, a boy and a girl, walking together on the road on Sunday. I didn't think anything of it—there were no classes on Sunday —I just happened to mention to the Twak Sunday night that I had seen the two of them.

Monday morning he had them both in his office. That afternoon we held a staff meeting, the Twak parading the boy in front of us, the teachers hurling questions at him. They wanted him to confess that he had had intercourse with the girl.

And of course he denied it. Why should they think that just because he was walking with her?

But the teachers weren't satisfied, they began screaming at him, Changuku, Changuku—I never did find out what Changuku meant, I guess it was too awful even to explain.

Then they brought in the girl. She was just a little thing—she couldn't have been more than twelve or thirteen—whose breasts were just beginning to develop. They started screaming at her—all except Mr. Ngubile, who kept saying that they were telling the truth, they hadn't done anything and we should forget the whole thing and just let them alone. Good for him.

And the little girl was crying now, shaking her head, No, no, they were just walking, they weren't doing anything.

118

Then the teachers each took up a stick and surrounded the boy in a circle. They began poking at him with short little thrusts, *Sema, sema,* speak, speak, and the boy crying *Hapana, hapana,* No, no. And now the pokes were becoming hits. They were beating the boy, harder now, all of them together, it was as though they had all gone mad, *Sema, sema,* with the boy trying to shield his body with his hands, and crying Stop, stop.

Suddenly the Twak lifted his arm and the beating stopped. He looked hard at the boy, grabbing the girl and pulling her next to him. Standing over them and glaring at them. One last chance. Did they want to admit?

They looked at each other, the boy and the girl. Then the boy nodded, We did it. And the girl bent her head and a great tear splashed on the floor.

They did it? They couldn't have, the girl was so young. It was because of the beating that they had admitted it. Couldn't they see that?

But the teachers were interrogating them now. Who else was having intercourse, how many were there? And they started calling off the names of the girls. Not just one or two, or four or five, but ten, twenty, twenty-two, all the girls of the school were involved.

So they called them in, all the girls, all twenty-two of them, and the Twak began telling them what he had heard, beginning in a very soft voice, Didn't you know you were being wicked? You, you changuku, he suddenly shrieked at them, his white teeth flashing under his black mustache.

And the girls began to cry and sniffle, short little sobs, Yes, nodding their heads, We have been wicked.

And who were their partners? the Twak wanted to know, and each one said a name, or two names, right on down the line. All except one girl, Tausi something-or-other, who stood there just shaking her head. She had been wicked, yes, but she wasn't saying who it was.

But no matter, they couldn't bother with her now, the boys were already here. Those who denied it would get the circle-beating treatment, the pokes becoming hits. And it wasn't long before they were all admitting it, all of them and their partners, except Tausi, who wasn't talking.

119

But no matter, she would get double, they were all going to the dining room now where they would be beaten in front of the whole school. So they rang the bell, the whole school flocking to the dining room, the sinners sitting together in the front as the Twak made a little speech introducing the culprits.

Then Mr. Ngubile stepped forward with his long swishing stick, beating each of them ten strokes, as they wriggled and sobbed and shrieked and moaned, boys and girls alike. Finally he came to the last one, Tausi, who, as she had refused to tell, would be beaten double. The stick came down three, four, five hard sharp strokes. Mr. Ngubile was sweating now, he looked tired, but he was continuing. His hand was about to come down for six, when suddenly Tausi began to moan and curse, turning and pointing up to him, Mr. Ngubile, as he stood above her, shrieking, He, he, he's the one, he's the one.

We went back to the office again, all the teachers and Tausi, and they made her say it again now, in front of us all, while Mr. Ngubile denied it, she was making the whole thing up, couldn't they see that, as I realized why he had wanted to forget the whole thing and just leave the first two alone. And of course we couldn't beat Mr. Ngubile the way we had beaten the boys until they had admitted it. So the Twak just adjourned the whole meeting.

And in the middle of the night, I heard a tremendous commotion, there was Tausi's father pounding on the Twak's door with a spear—What kind of a school are you running, you Changuku?—as the Twak ran to call all of us for help.

And in a few days Mr. Ngubile had his letter and the truck was appearing through the brick arch for him.

. . .

We were drifting into the hot season now, when the heat would come as the sun rose, and in the afternoons you'd see it sitting there on the mountains in waves. When you'd want to go inside and sleep in the afternoons—only once you lay down you couldn't get up again before evening.

The heat. Boys staring in the classroom, yawning and dozing. And you fought to tear the words from your mouth. And worse, you felt like going to sleep also, counting the minutes for the period to end, so you could get back home and lie down. And seeing Mbaliki there in the kitchen in only his underwear, standing over the stove, pushing a charcoal iron, a toothpick dangling between his teeth.

Waiting for the night, the evening, the sunset, when the heat would go down, when you'd have the one cool hour of daylight. Standing there in front of our houses, the sun sinking into the mountains as we threw the ball back and forth, the wives of the teachers sitting together in front of their houses sewing their mats, the children running around naked or standing at attention, waiting for us to drop the ball. That one cool hour of daylight which was the only relief we had.

The nights, taking our chairs and sitting outside late at night. Seeing the fires on the hills—they were burning the land now, preparing it for the rains that were due in the next couple of months. Listening to Radio South Africa and Lourenço Marques, Alan Jones of Pretoria to Mary Smith of Salisbury, the rock 'n' roll music and dedications. How far away it seemed, how far from Tanganyika, from Ndumulu School, how many worlds apart.

And realizing that the year was nearly over, the exam was not far off, and that I had a two-month vacation at the end of the year before the new term began. I would go south, to the land of the night music, the faraway world from Sue of Durban to Mark of Johannesburg.

Lately the Standard 8 boys were bringing us their compositions to correct. Their teachers never gave them any, and the exam was so close. They knew we gave the Standard 7 many compositions, would we correct theirs?

And as we glanced through their exercise books, we found there was no work in them. It was incredible. You'd see the date of one assignment, perhaps a grammar exercise, and then the next one would be a week later. They just hadn't been assigned any work for the whole year.

And it came to me then for the first time that we were the ones, Mike and I, who should have been teaching Standard 8, the highest class. We were the ones with the degrees, but somehow they just couldn't understand that we had been to university.

They had asked us once, I remember—looking at each other when we said, Yes, that we had been to university—Do you have degrees, and we nodded.

But why are you here? they wanted to know. No African with a degree would be teaching here at Ndumulu, Mr. Ngubile said. They would teach at a university, and have a car, a big house. Why didn't we? It must be a very funny degree.

And really that's what it was. That's really what they thought, that something must be the matter with our degrees. Because we taught at Ndumulu, because we lived next to them, because we lived the way they did—because of this our degrees were suspect, there must be something wrong with them.

But the really sad thing was that we weren't better teachers than they were because of our degrees. Because exactly how much university do you need to teach Standard 8? How much calculus do you need to teach parallelograms, how much Hemingway or Joyce to teach nouns and verbs? No, that wasn't the thing, it wasn't the degrees that made us more effective teachers than the Africans. No, it was the way we taught, the way we had been taught, really, the training we ourselves had had as schoolboys, where we had always been given homework, where we had always had to do it, where it had always been checked to see if we had done it. So that when we taught math, we gave them drill each night, when we taught English, we gave them plenty of reading and plenty of writing, the way we had learned when we were schoolboys.

Funny, though, they just didn't see it.

Funny about Mbaliki too. Little things at first, which we hadn't paid any attention to. Like his coming in late in the mornings and not having breakfast ready on time. Or not washing the dishes carefully. And he had taken a number of days off, first telling us another of his relatives had died, and then another one, and soon it was as though a relative was dying each week.

Then one afternoon he had come in drunk, hadn't cooked supper, just stood there ranting and raving about who were we to give him orders. He was leaving, he said, and he wasn't coming back tomorrow or any other day.

The next day he had returned, all apologies, promising it wouldn't happen again. I guess we should have sacked him then and there, but we didn't, we just started treating him very harshly and sternly. Do this, do that, bring the eggs, make the tea, boil the water. Only orders, nothing more. And we stopped going to his house, no more calling him Leek or any of that other rot. He was a servant and that's what we treated him like.

And, do you know, the odd thing was we didn't have any more

trouble after that. His work was good, he was always on time, his relatives stopped dying, he even would prepare fruit salads or special cakes that he hadn't made before, that we didn't even know he knew how to prepare.

So how do you figure it? Be mean, treat them harshly? Or let up and find yourself in heaps of difficulty? They were almost like little children. Or like slaves. Whoops, what am I saying? I really didn't mean that. Must be the heat, it was making us all edgy.

• • •

One night Mr. Twakatulu came up to us as we were throwing the baseball. It was dark now, and in fact it was really too dark to be throwing the ball around, but we usually kept at it these days until one of us got plunked between the eyes.

There was someone with him—very tall and thin—but in the shadows it was difficult to see who it was. We greeted the Twak and said *Oogonile* to the other man, as the Twak started bouncing up and down, his hands behind his back.

This man is Bwana Mchanga, he told us. He was a clerk of the court at Ushirika, and the Twak nodded his head. I began to wonder what he was leading up to.

Bwana Mchanga, he told us, had spent two hundred shillings of the court's money to pay for his daughter's school fees—which he had hoped to pay back at the end of this month when he got his paycheck. And he nodded again.

But now, they had discovered, a government official was coming tomorrow to check the books. If they found the two hundred shillings missing, it would mean prison for poor Bwana Mchanga.

Mmmm, we said sympathetically. Must say, it sounded a little fishy to me. School fees were an old sympathy line.

Mmmm, said the Twak, as if in agreement with our Mmmm.

Of course we now saw what it was. We'd lent money before to some of the teachers. And we had always gotten it back promptly —except from Mr. Ngubile, who had dillydallied around for about three months. But two hundred shillings. It had never been that much before.

The Twak didn't say anything now. He was just standing there, bouncing up and down and nodding his head. Why didn't he come out and ask us for it?

Feeling his embarrassment, I said, How much is it, again?

123

Two hundred shillings, he answered, still nodding his head.

I said, It's a lot of money, mmmm, and the Twak's nod turned into a Mmmm. He looked so pathetic standing there, unable or afraid to come right out with it and ask us for it.

Finally I said, O.K. We'll give you the two hundred. The Twak broke into *Asante sana, asante sana* and Bwana Mchanga began pumping our hands, *Asante sana, asante sana*.

So we went inside and fished out a hundred each—we could do it because we had just cashed a check last week. The Twak was still bouncing as we came back and handed him the money. We were giving it to him, the Twak, as Bwana Mchanga looked like a *mwizi* if I had ever seen one. They would return it all in three days, that's all it would be for they said.

Next morning, Mr. Mwadunda asked us if it was really true we had lent the money to Bwana Mchanga. I couldn't understand where he had already heard about it, but I had stopped wondering about these things a long time ago.

Yes, I said, we had.

He asked me why we hadn't consulted him before we had done it, so I told him the story about the Twak, and said the Twak was an honest man. Whatever else you wanted to say about him, he was honest.

But when Bwana Mchanga had lived down near the lake, Bwana Mchanga had borrowed money and then refused to pay it, Mr. Mwadunda said, and the villagers had finally gone and burned his house down. And he went away, shaking his head.

Later I told the story to Mike and we both agreed, all we could do was to wait and see.

Wednesday came and no money. Thursday we received a note that Bwana Mchanga had had some trouble getting the money today but he would have it for us the following Monday.

Monday came and no money, not even a note this time.

So I went to the Twak to ask him what was going on. He seemed very surprised that Bwana Mchanga hadn't returned the money yet. Mmmm. He nodded, He was sure there must be some mistake. We should send him a note. That would clear everything up.

Mmmm, I agreed.

So the Twak wrote something and sent a boy.

Soon the boy returned. He had been told that Bwana Mchanga

had just that minute gone out, and that he wouldn't be back until evening.

Mmmm, said the Twak again. He would see him the next day himself.

Mmmm, I said.

The next day the Twak was at our house. Bwana Mchanga had told him he was having some trouble collecting the money, but that he would most certainly give it to us soon.

Most certainly give it to us soon. What the hell did that mean! And suddenly I wanted to say, Look, Twak, this Bwana Mchanga is your friend. You are the one who told us to lend it to him. Now you get it back. What was this rot anyway!

Not that it was the money that was bothering me. I mean not the amount, it wasn't more than thirty dollars. No, it was the idea behind it, the feeling that it was beginning to sound like a great conspiracy, that they were fooling, cheating us. That we were strangers, that we were nothing more than soft touches, that they were putting something over on us.

And I thought back to Mbaliki and the way we had had to clamp down to get him to do his work right. The way we spoke to him now only when we gave him an order. No smiles, no laughing with him. Only business!

Was it the same now? Did we have to say no to everything that they asked us and stand there stony-faced and dignified? A brief shake of the head, like the Minister of Cooperatives and Finance?

Because if you did something for someone, or gave something to someone, the rest of them felt that you must do the same thing or give the same thing to everyone else. Like the way we had started lending money. Once Mr. Mwadunda had asked us, and then another time Mr. Mwaisunga. And then on down the line.

Or the time Mr. Mwambigila had asked me to lend him our radio. And I had been happy to give it to him. Then a few days later someone else had come and asked me for it, and I had given it to him too. And then another one, and another, until all of them had come around and asked me, as though they all had to get in on the act and would feel cheated if they didn't. Like a bunch of children.

The days passed, and still no word from Bwana Mchanga. A week. Two weeks.

Finally I confronted the Twak with the bitter truth, that I was becoming impatient with him and the whole business. So that Sunday he and I went to see him together.

And lo, there he was on the road. In fact he seemed very happy to see us, he ran up, *Oogonile, ndaga, isaga,* he had some pombe in his house, he had heard I was a great pombe drinker. But I stopped him cold in his tracks. We were having none of that today. We had come here to talk about the money which we had lent him. Which was over a month ago. Which he still hadn't returned.

He became very quiet, standing like a penitent little boy with his hands folded in front of him, looking down at the ground. Then looking up at me he began explaining that he had given it to a friend of his who wanted to buy a coat.

To a friend of his. Who did he think he was fooling? He looked down at his toes again.

I told him that he had one week to raise the money now. Or else I was going to take him to prison.

Yes, yes, he said. One week. That's all he needed, and we would have it.

On the way back to school the Twak told me that he was sure I would get the money now, I had frightened him very much. That's what was needed with a man like this. Mmmm, he nodded.

Mmmm, I said.

One week was all Bwana Mchanga needed, all right. For just as the week was up, we began to hear rumors that he had taken to his bed. That people passing his house had seen him deathly pale. So he must be near death. He had even told someone he wasn't sure just how much longer he would live.

Yet strangely enough he seemed to recover three days later after the week was passed. Nobody could figure it out. It must be some kind of magic, everyone said. And with that I knew how I was going to get that money back if everything else failed.

But first I had one more legitimate way that I wanted to try, and I rounded up the Twak and we went off again to find Bwana Mchanga. There he was on the road, he didn't look as though he had ever been sick in his whole life, much less last week when he had had a bout with death.

I told him that I wanted his paycheck at the end of the month, as he earned two hundred shillings. Then he could consider everything even.

126

Surprisingly enough he agreed to it. In fact he seemed very happy about the whole thing. So we shook hands, it was only two more weeks to payday and I wondered why I hadn't thought of this before and saved myself all that aggravation.

Only the morning of payday Mbaliki woke me up. Bwana Mchanga wasn't planning to pay. He was going to Tukuyu himself, to pick up his money, and then to Mbeya with it.

How did he know?

That's what people were saying.

Was he sure?

For an answer he ran over to Mr. Mwadunda. Yes, Mr. Mwadunda had heard the same thing. Only he hadn't wanted to say anything to me. My God, how these people got their information was truly astounding. They knew everything about everything and about everybody.

All right, I said to the Leek. This is it. The old plan of the last resort. Get me a pack of matches and some pieces of paper.

What will you do? he called. How will you get it?

Never you mind, I called back to him. But I'll get the money all right.

Actually I wasn't exactly sure how I was going to get it. Or really even what I was going to do to get it. But I knew I was going to do something. Mr. Biboko and the cracked cup, Mr. Ngubile's friend who had been bewitched by an Indian for not paying his debt, the boys staring at me wide-eyed and unbelievingly as the ice cubes melted in front of their eyes. And poor Bwana Mchanga suddenly, mysteriously taking to his bed. And even more suddenly recovering when his week was up. Well, they were now going to see some real American magic.

Only Bwana Mchanga wasn't at home when I arrived. Instead there were two little old men with a bowl of pombe on the table. He had just gone out, they said. About a minute ago. No doubt he had seen me coming.

Mmmm, I thought, This called for a minor alteration. But no matter, no serious problem, as we said our *Oogoniles* and *Ndagas*.

Now I began in a very serious voice: I have come here on some very important business. I wanted them to know that no harm would come to them, that they shouldn't be afraid of what they were going to see. They stared at me as though transfixed.

And with that I took one of the pieces of paper I had brought, waving it in front of the two little old men with very exaggerated gestures, the way a magician performs in front of children. And very slowly, very deliberately, I took out a match, bending down on the ground, lighting one corner of the paper.

And as I did, I began to blow softly, calling out Ahh, ahh in a fairly loud voice, so that anyone around would be certain to hear. And now chanting, Mchanga, Mchanga, and throwing in the words *mwizi*, thief, and *mwongo*, liar. And *mtu mbayba*, bad man. *Mungu*, God, and *kufa* which means die.

Suddenly the two old men bolted past me out the door, leaving it half open. Looking out after them, I saw that a crowd of people had gathered outside, staring in at me as though they too were transfixed.

And now, realizing the American magic was working so well, the Great Transfixer stalked outside, with the burning paper in his hand. And I bellowed a great loud Ahh Mchanga, thrusting my hand out at the crowd. A sudden gasp hissed through them, and they fell back a few steps.

My paper was almost out now, and I wasn't exactly certain what I would do next, when Bwana Mchanga suddenly appeared, and started coming toward me through the crowd. Quick I hurled what was left of the paper at him—of course it went out—as he raised his hands in front of his face, as if to fend off the evil spirit of the paper, the crowd gasping again.

I began shouting at him in Swahili, calling him a *mwizi* and a *mwongo*. I wanted my money. And right now. And if he ran off to Mbeya as I had heard he might, I couldn't be responsible for what might happen to him.

And suddenly he broke into sobs. Please, please forgive him, but he didn't have any money, he was just a poor man. My God, he was quite an actor himself, Bwana Mchanga. But he wasn't fooling me.

And with that I took my second piece of paper, raising my hand, waving it about and wailing Mchanga, Mchanga, Mchanga, *mwongo*, Mchanga *mwizi*, throwing in a *mungo* and a *kufa*, so he would be sure I meant business. Then bending down again, lighting the edge, and giving out with Ahh, ahh, as the crowd stared at me in disbelief, the Great Transfixer.

Quite suddenly I felt him touching my arm very softly, and heard him say very quietly that he had the money. Come, he would give it to me.

I couldn't believe my ears. Was it true, could it really be this easy?

So I very dramatically blew out the flame and followed him through the crowd who fell back now to let me pass. Apparently no one wanted to get too close to the Great Transfixer.

He was leading me along the road to Ushirika now, where the court was. And the crowd—there must have been over a hundred of them, it was something truly amazing—following like a retinue, but at a safe distance.

Yet somehow I still couldn't believe that I was going to get the money, it just couldn't be this easy. Any minute I was expecting him to tell me that he had lost the key, or to find that the safe was empty inside.

But no, he had the key. Into the courthouse and opening the safe and there it was. Two hundred shillings. He counted it out and put it smack in my hand. Finished. I took it without a word and put it in my pocket.

He followed me back outside, and suddenly stuck out his hand for me to shake as if to say, Well, are you satisfied, are we friends now, is everything going to be all right?

But somehow I didn't want everything to be all right. I just didn't want to let him off that easy. Not after all the aggravation I had been through.

So I motioned all the villagers over to me. Come close, I called, but they wouldn't come too close. They stood around me, off a little way, while I spoke to them.

I recounted all the things Bwana Mchanga had done, how he had first come that night with the Twak, disturbing us, begging for the money. Telling us about his school fees for his daughter, saying if we didn't help him, he might go to prison.

And how we had helped him, giving him the money without a moment's hesitation—which wasn't exactly true, but how did they know that?—without a word of complaint.

And all the times we had tried to get it back. All the stories he had told, how he had told us he had lent the money to his friend, our money, which we had given him, how he had pretended to take to his bed. To cheat us.

Two months. Two months, I shouted at them, as they drew back. Two months we had waited.

And suddenly I stopped and asked them in my Ahh Mchanga

voice whether I could be responsible for what might happen to a man like this—even if he had finally given me back the money. What about all the weeks I had spent trying to get it? They stood there without a word, without a sound.

I am going now, I said. And to Bwana Mchanga I said that he would be all right, I thought, but that possibly—I couldn't say for certain, I wouldn't take the responsiblility—possibly he might come down with a severe stomach ache that night when the sun went down. But he was not to worry. It wouldn't be serious, even though it might be severe. And it would be over by morning.

And with that I left him there staring after me, the crowd opening in a little path for me—like the Red Sea parting for Moses. Turning their heads and following me with their eyes now, like little children.

And walking through them like that, I almost felt the way Moses must have when the Sea opened up for him. I still couldn't believe it had been so easy, I knew it violated everything that I had come here thinking and believing in. Really what I still believed in, I guess.

And I thought how easy it would be to rule these people, to be their leader by being high-handed and supercilious, gruff, short-tempered, but mostly by being aloof and haughty. Like the Minister of Cooperatives and Finance. Because they were so easily swayed, so easily led, just like a group of little children. What they seemed to respect more than anything was some great chief whom they could listen to, who just ordered them what to do.

And it was sad to discover this.

. . .

After the Great Shift, I thought certainly Mr. Twakatulu would give us English to teach in Standard 8. Instead he gave me math in 8B. He taught 8A himself.

To find out where he was in the book, how fast he was going, how much he would assign the boys each night, I began stopping at the office or at his home every few days to check with him. He told me that he liked to give sums each night, but they took him so long to correct that he only gave work once or twice a week. And oh, by the way, how was I going to explain this—the volume of a cylinder —or that—the Pythagorean theorem? And it didn't take me very

130

long to discover that the poor Twak knew very little math at all.

One afternoon he showed me a piece of paper which he said was an application for his Cambridge School Certificate Examination—whatever that meant. Would I mind correcting his mistakes and checking that each item was filled in correctly?

He said that he had been thinking of taking the exam this year. It would be great *heshima*—prestige—if he passed, but he would have to study very hard. There were three subjects that he had selected—Swahili, which he said he knew he knew, biology, which he said he thought he knew, and British Constitution, to which he could only lamely shake his head.

British Constitution. Why had he chosen that? I wondered. Then he asked me, Did I think I might be able to help him with it?

With what? British Constitution? What did I know about British Constitution? But I said O.K. I would try to help him. However little I knew, I knew it must be more than he knew.

Then he asked me if I could lend him three hundred shillings, two hundred for the application fee and one hundred for the British Constitution textbook. He could pay me back at the end of the month when he received his paycheck.

At the end of the month. When he received his paycheck. Where had I heard that before? And I couldn't help smiling in spite of myself. How could he have the nerve to ask me for that after Bwana Mchanga? Except that seeing him staring at me so earnestly —as though it could never dawn on him what I was thinking—and realizing too that three hundred shillings was almost his entire month's salary, I knew how badly he must want this.

And maybe it was stupid—in fact I know it was, I should have learned my lesson before. All the more so because it would only be a question of time before he gave up anyway. Because I had tutored Mr. Mwadunda last term, who had told me he was teaching math to Standard 6 but that he had never understood rectangles and triangles.

And at first I thought he had been kidding. But he wasn't, I soon found out, he didn't know a damn thing. (And I wondered why the boys in Standard 7 didn't know any math.) And he had quit after two weeks, saying that he wanted to concentrate on another field. Which meant that he wanted to drink pombe at Ushirika. Some other field.

Anyway, I thought about all this when the Twak asked me, before I gave him the money.

In a few weeks the textbook came. A fat, black hard-covered thing with about five hundred pages. With very small print. One flip through it and I knew we were in for trouble. If the Twak could last two weeks with this stuff he would be doing well.

So I began to tutor the Twak. I would come to his house three afternoons a week, and he would take out the fat black book. But somehow the Twak couldn't get the hang of it. He would sit there nodding, Yes, yes, but when I asked him a question he'd sit there with the most puzzled and pained expression on his face—like that time I had called him for walking, playing basketball.

After a couple of lessons, I realized what it was. He couldn't understand the English. It was too difficult for him. Which meant I would have to go over the chapter aloud with him the first time, writing down all the new words like "liability" or "hereditary monarchy," and explaining the catch phrases to him, such as, the Queen reigns but does not rule, or the Prime Minister is to his Cabinet as the sun is to the planets.

And I would tell him to go back and reread it to himself that night, the next day we would discuss it together. And the day after that I would test him on the questions which they had at the end of each chapter, and have him write out his answers for homework.

Only at this rate I knew we could never complete the book. So I checked off what I thought were the most important chapters—which cut it by two thirds—and we tried to do the best we could, while each day I expected him to tell me that he had had enough, that he wanted to concentrate on another field.

But the Twak did not give up. Each day he would be ready, his reading completed, or his questions ready to be answered. And it was so tedious, so torturous, reading the chapter with him, paragraph by paragraph, line by line, word by word. It would take four or five hours each lesson. And I thought of how it must be for him at night when I left, when he would have to spend another three or four hours rereading the way I had told him to do, or struggling with the questions at the end of each chapter. I could picture him at his table, huddled over his kerosene lamp, wrinkling his brows and pulling at his long mustache until all hours of the morning.

As we went on, he would stop by my house in the afternoons,

waiting for me outside until I finished whatever I might be doing. One Saturday I found him waiting for me as I returned from Tukuyu, sitting there on the doorstep of my house, his legs dangling in front of him, looking like an overgrown schoolboy.

It would be longer each night now, and I would be coming four and five times a week. And in the middle of our lesson his wife would bring in tea for us, and we would talk over our cups. Sometimes he would ask me about math, as we had a kind of common ground now. How was I teaching interest and per cent? Did I think he was giving the boys enough homework each night? Were they working hard enough? Did they stand a good chance of passing the exam?

And I was glad he felt now that he could ask me these things. And gladder still that he cared enough about the boys to ask. It seemed so sad though, that as much as he wanted to help them— and he really did want to—he just couldn't see how much more it would help the Standard 8 boys if they let us, Mike and me, teach them, instead of giving us P.E.

Yet I could begin to see now what it was, or really why it was that they preferred to teach Standard 8 themselves. These teachers like the Twak had been teaching these subjects for five, ten or maybe more years. And now Mike and I, two strangers who had never taught before in Tanganyika—or anyplace else—coming here expecting to take over what they had been doing all their teaching lives. No matter how much it might help the boys. . . .

And of course this was something we could never say to the Twak or to any of them. Just as I could never tell the Twak that giving sums once or twice a week was just not enough practice for the boys. Or just as I could never tell him that keeping the boys in class every afternoon and every night with no free time, with no exercise, wasn't the way to do it either.

As the exam drew nearer, we would sit there late into the night, Mrs. Twakatulu waddling in with a big tray of supper, putting it down on the table as we took a break. And I thought of the first time I had eaten at the Twak's house—it seemed so long ago— when everything had been so strange, so new. And now I would actually look forward to these suppers, I would say to Mrs. Twakatulu that I would go back to America telling everyone about her cooking, and she would shake with laughter.

And I noticed, as I was eating there nearly every night, that they would always serve me meat, knowing that I liked it. And knowing too how rarely they themselves ate meat because they couldn't afford it—not more than twice a week, if that. Maybe it was the Twak's way of saying thank you to me.

Then with about two weeks to go before his exam, the Twak announced that he was taking a two-week leave of absence from teaching to prepare himself for his exam. He had obtained permission from the educational officer. And I marveled how he could just take off like that if he really wanted to help the boys. How could he do it to them with their exam not even a month away? And I marveled also at the educational officer's granting him permission. Just who was going to teach his classes?

Oh, yes, the Twak said, we would just combine 8A and 8B. I could teach math to both classes together.

So that's what I had to do, teach both of them together. We were on the last chapter of the book, graphs: A man leaves Town A at 9 A.M. and goes at the rate of 10 miles an hour for four hours. He rests an hour and then continues his journey for another two hours at 20 miles per hour. How far had he traveled at the end of this time? At what time does he reach town B if it is 50 miles from A? Show this in a graph.

Problems like that. And I'd show them how to draw the axes, putting time on the horizontal, speed or rate on the vertical. And marking x's at the points they were plotting. Yet for some reason these kids couldn't do them. They just couldn't seem to get the idea of what they were drawing. They'd write down the wrong rates or the wrong times, or they'd begin time at 10 miles per hour, not 9 o'clock. Or they'd plot 9:45 between 10 and 11 o'clock.

And soon I realized that most of these kids couldn't tell time; that was the basis of the problem right there. But I'd have to make sure they understood, because graphs were very important for the exam they had told us. Which meant that I had to begin with telling time, and I had to speak in Swahili because Swahili time begins at 7 A.M., not midnight, that's when they say the day begins, when the sun rises, they call that the first hour, one o'clock, not seven.

It also meant that I had to teach them at night, since time-telling took up nearly the whole morning periods. The same problems, a man leaves at 8 A.M. and travels at a steady rate of 20 miles an hour for three hours. He rests for a half hour and continues at a rate of 10 miles an hour. At what time does he reach Town B, 10 miles away? Over and over, night after night.

And finally by the end of the first week, they began to show signs of understanding. By the middle of the second week they actually understood what they were doing. But they were so, so slow.

So I'd start to give them quick one-problem, five-minute tests. Boom, and I'd collect them before some of them had even got their points plotted or their axes drawn. And some of them would actually hand in a blank sheet of paper. They'd plead with me, those who hadn't finished, please would I give them another chance, another test. So I'd have someone who had finished the test draw that graph on the board, and then quick before he'd even sit down, I'd start them on another test, one problem, five minutes.

Late at night, after I left, they would be scribbling over their desks in the dim light of a hurricane lamp. Once I woke up in the middle of the night and noticed a light coming from the 5A classroom. I looked at my watch, 3 A.M., put on my slippers and went to see. There inside were groups of three and four of them huddled around the little hurricane lamps, stuck into the farthest corners because they did not want anyone to see the light since they were supposed to be in bed. Scribbling over the graphs that we had done that night in class. I almost cried seeing them there, like that.

The Twak's exam was on a Monday morning. The Friday before he had come over to my house and handed me the three hundred shillings I had lent him. He was going to Mbeya today, he said. That's where the exam was. He would stay there and rest up for the weekend, get himself a hotel room and study there Saturday and Sunday without fear of being disturbed. Perhaps I could come there tomorrow and help him study the last two days.

Sure, I said. The final weekend.

He was in his hotel room, sprawled out in a chair, his book open, when I found him. There in a small dingy room with a little washbasin and a sagging bed, with cracked paint and cobwebs on the wall, and a dim light bulb hanging from the ceiling. And seeing him there like that, two months and three hundred shillings after he had begun, studying as hard as ever, not even thinking for a moment what a dump he was staying in—I suddenly had this great warm feeling come over me, that the Twak was really all right after all.

That with all his madness, his staff meetings, his bumblings, his screaming, his beatings, his cracked cup, nevertheless there was something to be said for this man who had studied every day, every night, for the last two months, who hadn't quit, who hadn't given in.

Coming to the school at the beginning of the year, new, with Mr. Biboko trying to take his place. And with us arriving there at the same time. The first white men he had ever worked with, I am sure. And that first night our running off, leaving him standing there alone in front of our house. Our friendship with Mr. Biboko. Catching me in the dining room with him that night, as he was speaking to the boys, telling them God only knows what. How much courage it must have taken for him to come there and speak to me like that, warning me about Mr. Biboko.

And now seeing him here in this dingy little room, I almost felt like putting my arm around his shoulders and saying, Look, you deserve something better than this. Let me take you to a good hotel. I'll even pay myself.

But I didn't. Instead I studied with him Saturday night and all day Sunday. Then I left for school. He would come tomorrow afternoon, he said, right after his exam.

Monday afternoon I saw him ambling through the brick arch, bouncing over to my house. He thrust a paper in front of me. The exam questions—ten of them. He had to choose any five. Looking down at them . . . four, five, six, seven, eight questions that he knew. That we had covered. All right from the chapters we had done. My God, I had psyched out the test perfectly.

The Twak was nodding his head furiously. Yes, yes, how had I known the exam, how had I known to pick these chapters? He couldn't understand it.

Mmm, I said, trying to keep myself from breaking out into a great grin. By God, I really had done it.

Mmm, he said, as if in answer to my mmm.

The next morning he came to see me as I went to math class. The boys had said they were doing graphs now. Did I think he could come and sit in on my class? He had never understood graphs very well himself.

So he did. We kept the classes combined, the Twak sitting there in the back, as attentively as the boys, scribbling on a little pad. And all the rest of the days that week through the exam.

136

The exam—the boys' exam. There was an Indian school from Tukuyu taking it with our boys. Three carloads of them. With all their teachers and a group of Indian parents. All wearing shoes, new shirts and trousers, sitting down outside the dining room, the parents passing out little sweets to them, talking only to each other, the teachers walking around saying a word of encouragement to each of them.

Seating them inside the dining room. A thin little Indian boy looks up at me. Does he have to sit next to an African? One of the Indian teachers, hearing him, runs up to him hissing, Shh, don't say that here. As if it would be all right to say it some other place.

And now seeing our boys, our Standard 8's, coming in and sitting down. In their white uniforms, barefoot. Where are the parents to give them some sweets, where are the teachers to give them encouragement? Thinking of all the nights they had spent, studying to midnight and one o'clock. The group of them huddled around the hurricane lamp until three in the morning. Having no idea how they had been deprived, no idea how much they deserved.

.    .    .

We hadn't thought anything of the demonstrations at first. Just something we had read in the paper about some students in Dar es Salaam marching on the Embassy and that more demonstrations were expected throughout the country. Then hearing on the radio about Tshombe and American imperialism, American militarists massacring Africans. And Mr. Kambona, the Foreign Minister, revealing a letter that proved the American government together with the South African and Portuguese governments were plotting to overthrow the government of Tanganyika.

Soon some of the local TANU officials began stopping at the school, speaking to the boys about the Congo and the Plot. And they would say to us, Mike and me, personally we were very good people, we had helped them very much, but they didn't know about our government. That Mr. Lyndon, he was very fierce. Then they would start about the Congo and Tshombe, American imperialists murdering their African brothers. And the Plot, America conspiring with Tanganyika's enemies.

But the Plot has not been proved, I said. Mr. Kambona refuses to reveal where he received the letter from.

No matter, they would say, laughing and shaking their heads.

These are *mambo ya siasa*—political matters—and we ordinary people cannot be expected to understand them, the way our leaders do. You both are very good, but your government is very bad, and they would laugh and slap palms.

One Saturday in Tukuyu I bumped into Martin Martinson. Had we heard what his tea workers were saying about us? That we were spies, Mike and I, that was why we had come to Tanganyika? That wás the reason we were so friendly and drank pombe with them at Ushirika. To learn their secrets. I could just picture them sitting over their bowls, nodding their heads in between sips, Mmmm, spies, yes. Taking another long gulp. Mmmm, spies.

And I couldn't help thinking about the things you read at home, Communist agitators trying to stir up trouble for Americans. Was it happening right here in Tukuyu? Except that there were no Communists here, probably no one knew what a Communist was. Not even the one who had begun these spy rumors, whoever he was.

One afternoon we awoke from an afternoon nap and found the whole school gone. I mean no one was there. No students. No teachers. We walked up the road to some of the villagers who were sitting outside their huts. *Mandamano,* Tukuyu, they said. A demonstration in Tukuyu. That's where they all had gone.

A demonstration in Tukuyu. An anti-American demonstration. That's what it must be. That was why no one had told us about it. That was why the Twak had just packed up the school and pulled them all into Tukuyu while we were sleeping. So we wouldn't find out about it.

Still it wasn't too late. It might be very interesting. We could walk to Ushirika, maybe a car would be passing.

Sure enough, as we arrived a car passed. A big one, with two men inside. We waved it down and it was our friend Mr. Mapunda, the local TANU chairman and another man whom I didn't know. They were both wearing those long robes that they wore at ceremonies.

We're going to the *mandamano,* they said. Why weren't we there already?

Missed our ride, we said, as we jumped in the back.

We began talking about school. The other man told me that his son was in my class, Lufingo Mbumulu. Oh, Lufingo, I said. (A good boy but was he stupid!) Are you Lufingo's father? I said. The man nodded his head and smiled. Then they said that they knew how hard we were working at Ndumulu and that they were very pleased we had come here to Tanganyika. We were helping them very much.

Soon we were in Tukuyu, everyone marching up and down with their bands blaring, the white shirts covering the streets and going in all directions. Judging by the size, it seemed like a very important *mandamano*. Then we noticed a special line of people walking down the middle of the street, everyone stepping back out of their way. There at the head was Mr. Mapunda, with Mr. Mbumulu and some other officials, all the bigwigs and government officials, the magistrate, the medical officer, all in long robes. And behind them were other government officials; there were Moses, Simon and Hebron. And Medson. They were all carrying signs and waving. Now they saw us, Hebron and Medson, they were calling to us, smiling, *Karibu, karibu,* and Mr. Mapunda was motioning toward us, they wanted us to join them in the march.

We started forward but Mike stopped me in my tracks, pointing to the signs that they were all carrying. What they said was AMERICA GO HOME. AMERICAN SPIES. AMERICAN IMPERIALISTS. TSHOMBE AMERICAN STOOGE. These demonstrators, our friends, they were demonstrating against us.

So we just stayed on the side of the street, waving to them as they passed, and let ourselves be pushed over to the field where a platform had been assembled.

The first speaker came up to speak, it was Mr. Mbumulu, *Uhuru,* and the crowd, *Uhuru.* Then speaking in short quick Swahili, as though he were very angry, so quickly that I couldn't catch what he was saying. Only a few words, Tshombe, America, spies.

Then the next one, *Uhuru.* The crowd roaring back, *Uhuru.* About America again, this time not so quickly so I could understand him. That America wanted to capture Tanganyika, they must be very careful . . . as the crowd roared its approval.

The next speaker was Mr. Mapunda. American spies, they were all around us, they were trying to learn our secrets. We must be very careful, we must look for them everywhere, they are right among us. And the crowd started turning their heads, looking to see if there were any spies among them.

Involuntarily I turned my head too, looking across all the black

139

faces. Suddenly I realized that we were the only white people there, Mike and I. That when they had been talking about spies and being careful, they meant us.

Then another one was talking, just really summing up what the others had said. And finally bellowing to the crowd, And what should be done to these American spies when we catch them? And the crowd roaring back, *Tuwafukuze nyumbani*—We should chase them back home. And with that a great roar went up, and the speakers raced off the platform, the crowd sweeping behind them. And they were heading toward us.

And somehow I couldn't believe that it was really happening, it couldn't really be true. It seemed so fantastic, our friends, Simon and Medson, Mr. Mapunda and Mr. Mbumulu, who had given us the ride today, saying how much they appreciated our being here, how we were helping them very much. And they were the ones who had made these speeches, who had inflamed all the crowd. They were walking toward us now. And I was thinking, My God, we are going to be attacked.

But we weren't attacked. The first one to reach us was Mr. Mapunda, who said he wanted us to understand that what they were saying had nothing to do with us, Mike or me. We were their friends, they all knew that. It was the government they were against. They were the spies. Not us. They all greatly appreciated what we were doing at Ndumulu, they knew how hard we were working, and how much we were trying to help them.

And me standing there with my mouth falling open, trying to understand what he was saying. Not knowing what to say, just feeling shaky all over as though I was suddenly going to burst out laughing or crying, I wasn't sure which. Trying to understand it, to understand that they felt we were really their friends, not their enemies. To understand that there were two Americans here—probably the only Americans they had ever known or seen—but that somehow, because they all knew us and liked us, we could not really be Americans. That we and Americans were two different things.

Trying to understand. It was so strange, almost mad. Yes, mad, that's what it was, mad. It was all madness, not just the demonstration, but all of it. The school staff meetings, beatings, marching, Mr. Biboko and his magic, the transfers. The boys fighting and stealing one day, friends the next. The drinking at Ushirika day

140

after day. The way villagers would laugh to us and smile, seeing us drinking with them, hearing us speaking Kinyakusa.

But what was behind that laugh, what was behind that smile? I can hear that sound of their laughter, see that smile, but what is behind it, what does it mean? That they like us because we have made an old man happy by speaking Kinyakusa, because we have drunk their pombe?

And it suddenly occurred to me that we had been with these people nearly a year now, that we had lived in their village, had eaten their food, had taught their children. But what did we really know of them? Nearly a year and what had we learned? If anything, that we weren't close to them at all, that we seemed to become farther apart the longer we lived there. Nearly a year, and I am just beginning now to realize how little about them, about it all, how little I understand.

# III

AND THEN I AM OFF, walking through the brick arch, with Fedson carrying my little overnight bag into which I have crammed everything that I think I might possibly need for the next two months. Two months, that's how long my vacation is, and I am heading south, I want to go right to the tip, all through Rhodesia and South Africa, all the way to Capetown.

But first I am going to visit Fedson Mwandemele and his family. Fedson, who is one of my students, my brightest student, whose village is on the way south, Kapolo, just over the Tanganyika border into Malawi, just a short walk from Kyela, he has said, and just north of Karonga, the capital of northern Malawi, where the road begins. The same road which leads into the Great Northern Road through Zambia, into Rhodesia, and then South Africa.

And all the other boys on the road, in their white uniforms, the boxes of their belongings on their heads, are all stopping to shake my hand and wish me a pleasant journey, as Fedson has told them that I am going to his home. He has written to his family, he says, they are all expecting me, his father who is a priest, his mothers, all his brothers and sisters.

And the villagers along the way, calling to me, *Oogonile, ndaga,* am I going home now that the examination is finished? As if home is the next village, perhaps, or even as far as Dar es Salaam, a day or two's journey on the bus.

At Ushirika, waiting for the bus from Mbeya, which will take us south to Kyela. More villagers coming up to me, Where am I going? And I saying, Down to Kapolo, and looking at Fedson, Is that the name of the village? Kapolo?

And the villagers laughing, But how will I get to Kapolo from Kyela? And saying to them that it is just a short walk from Kyela, that's what Fedson had said.

But do I know how far it is from Kyela to Kapolo? And I shake my head, beginning to get the feeling that there is something Fedson hasn't told me.

But it is too late now, there is the bus, not the regular bus this time, a private one, really just an old truck into which the owner has built seats. It is filled with schoolboys from Tukuyu, singing at the top of their lungs and leaning out the windows, all going home for their vacation.

I don't see how we can possibly squeeze in, but there is Fedson, pushing himself through the door, and the driver calling to me to come and sit up in front with him. He knows me, he says, we have drunk pombe together once at Ushirika. And the shouts of the little boys, crowding around the bus and thrusting up hands into the windows, *Mayai, machungwa, mandazi, ndizi,* as I smile my thanks to him. It is always an honor to sit next to the driver.

Then he toots his horn, and the people standing just outside the windows call their final goodbyes, and the little boys who have swarmed around the bus fly off now in all directions as the bus lumbers off.

And after a few hundred yards, you can see that we are on the top of a ridge of mountains like the edge of a great wall, and out to the left a great drop. And there below us is the lake, Lake Nyasa, shiny blue, surrounded by the flat land that stretches below as far as the eye can see. For in the thirty miles from Ushirika to Kyela the land level has dropped from five thousand feet down to sea level.

The bus joggles on, the schoolboys singing again in the back, they are going home to their villages to see their families for the first time in how many months. And I cannot help smiling, I almost feel as they do myself, the last day of school, the first day of vacation, the beginning of the long holiday.

Then a boy is banging on the window, which separates the back of the bus from the front, as the bus pants to a stop. The driver is climbing out, up to the top of the bus and throwing down the boy's box. *Mugonege,* goodbye, the boy calls to his friends inside, and comes around the front to me, sticking a hand through the window, Goodbye, sir, even if he doesn't go to Ndumulu. Everyone knows about the two American teachers.

We bump on, winding around curves, the sun peering in through the window. We are steadily going down, the boys singing more loudly now, more excited the closer they come to their homes. Then another banging on the window, another stop, the driver jumping out, more goodbyes, another hand sticking through the window, Goodbye, sir.

Soon the road is flat—we have already descended the five thousand feet—and it is becoming very hot. There are mud huts on the side of the road nearly hidden by banana trees, and bent old men in white sheets standing in the furrows, digging with hoes, small boys beside them. They are doing their last planting as the rains are late, the driver tells me, they are expected any day now. And the burned land around us, smoke rising off in the distance paling the sun, the hot red clay of the road, the dust that the bus swirls behind it rising up like two fantails and settling into a great cloud.

We turn to the left, down another dirt road—there are some mud buildings and a market, an open field, with some people squatting on the ground selling goods. Just this marketplace and a few mud buildings. This is Kyela. And the bus stops.

The boys have climbed out and are pulling their boxes down. Some men come over to me as I stand by the side of the bus, *Broo, broo,* how is Ndumulu? Don't I remember them? We have met at Ushirika where we once drank a bowl of pombe together.

So we greet each other, *Oogonile, oogonile, Ndaga, ndaga.* And Fedson comes up carrying our bags as the other boys stop to shake my hand, Goodbye, sir.

Maybe we should rent bicycles for the journey, Fedson says, as riding would be easier than walking, and he leads me over to one of the mud huts where some men are sitting outside drinking pombe.

*Isaga,* they say to me, but No, thank you, we are about to leave for Kapolo.

Ahh, they nod, yes. A very long journey. I look at Fedson. What's this about a long journey? Just how far is it, Fedson?

Fifteen miles, he says. Fifteen miles. And you said it was short —wondering to myself why I hadn't had enough sense to ask him this before I left.

144

So we start talking about the bicycles—what else can I do?—for two dollars they say they will ride both of us. And I am just wondering how we can carry our bags if we are riding on the back—not that mine is big, it's just an overnight bag, but Fedson has a big box—when two girls appear. One is about fourteen, just beginning to develop breasts, pretty and small, and the other, her younger sister maybe, tiny, she can't be more than seven or eight.

They kneel down near Fedson and touch hands, *Oogonile,* in just the softest, the gentlest way, that little one especially, and Fedson tells me they are his sisters, they have just come from Kapolo to meet us. From Kapolo. That means that they have come fifteen miles.

They kneel down to me, *Oogonile* in that soft voice, and Fedson says that the big one is Bumi and the little one Annie. I begin to speak to them in Swahili, but Fedson says that they do not know Swahili—only Nyakusa and Tumbuka, the language of northern Malawi—but Bumi knows a little English.

So I ask her, How was your journey? And she tells me that they left their house early this morning. Now that they have greeted us, they will walk back. Which adds up to thirty miles according to my arithmetic. Those two young girls.

Then Bumi says that they will carry our bags for us, so that we can ride on the bicycles. I look at Fedson questioningly, they don't really mean it, do they, how can they carry our loads fifteen miles? And the little one is so tiny. But there they are bending down, with Fedson lifting his box onto little Annie's head—mine is small enough so I can carry it in my lap. Straightening up now, standing, Annie holding the box with one hand, *Mugonege,* goodbye, to us, walking away down the road together now, Annie balancing the box on her head, no hands, that little girl, the box almost as big as she is.

Then we climb on the back of the bicycles, I holding my overnight bag in my lap, and the men begin pedaling. We should reach the River Songwe in about two hours, they say, which is about half the distance. And my watch says one o'clock, and the sun is hot overhead.

Soon the main road stops and we turn down a little dirt path, very narrow, like a footpath, whizzing down it, the banana trees on either side, with mud huts behind them, half hidden by the leaves.

And people now, half naked, are standing by the side of the road, staring at us, so close that I can reach out and touch their black chests and curly black hair.

*Oogonile,* I call out, and they answer back in a chorus, *Oogonile,* as we shoot past them, smiling and laughing now, buzzing very excitedly to each other, *Mzungu, mzungu,* White man, white man.

The road is curving, the same flatness around each bend, the same banana trees on the side, the same huts half hidden behind them, the same people half naked staring after us, *Mzungu, mzungu.* And now there are cattle, lying on the ground in front of the huts, six or seven of them together next to a smoky fire of leaves and twigs, as if they must all be diseased or dying.

But no, Fedson says, it is to smoke out their ticks and flies.

Then cutting off the road, we are walking the bicycles now, tramping between banana trees, past huts with naked little children running behind us and shrieking as though they have never seen a white man before.

Suddenly we come to a clearing, a great, flat field stretching out before us. We stand there resting for a moment, staring out at it, it looks three, maybe four miles to the other side, all bare, with nothing but a few trees every hundred yards or so. Fedson points to it, Yes, that is where we must go, just past the other side is the Songwe, the border of Tanganyika and Malawi.

So we begin, and it seems to stretch forever, and we the only people to be seen now. The sun beating down on us, with every hundred yards or so a lone tree, so flat, nothing there, nothing. And it occurs to me that this is Africa, the Africa that comes to mind when you say Africa, these miles and miles of open, of nothingness, only a tree scattered every few hundred yards. And I have this weird feeling that somehow we have lost the road, that we have taken the wrong fork, that instead of taking the path to the border, we have taken a road that leads a thousand years back into the past. Only the flatness, the bareness, and I am the first white man ever to cross here.

Then the trees on the other side begin edging closer. We are approaching them now, leaving the field behind us, just as flat, just as bare. At the other side, cutting off the path now, between two small huts, more banana trees, and we find ourselves at the edge of a hill. And looking down, there is a river below us, not more than

146

ten yards wide, brown, flowing very slowly. The Songwe. Across on the other side, Malawi.

There on the other side stands a little boy, a torn black cloth wrapped around his skimpy shoulders, covering his body to the tops of his thighs. He holds a bamboo pole in his hand and stands next to a dugout, a bark canoe. One of the men yells something across at him, and he steps into his canoe, pushing it off the bank with his pole. But instead of pushing off straight toward us, he pushes upstream and suddenly the bow of his canoe is swept right around by the current so that he has actually come in a semicircle, his canoe sitting parallel to our bank now, as he pulls himself in with his pole and waits for us to climb down the hill.

Fedson is first and we pass the bicycles down to him. The canoe is too small for all of us, so the boy pushes off with Fedson and they unload the bicycles on the other side. Then Fedson takes the bamboo pole and steps back into the canoe by himself, leaving the little boy standing on the shore. Only he does not push off as the little boy did, instead he heads the bow straight across toward us, to the other side, and the current hits him broadside, swinging him back into shore and nearly upsetting the canoe. And the little boy standing there on the bank doubles over and howls with laughter, slapping himself on the thigh.

Next time Fedson pushes off the way the boy did. And then we are stepping into the canoe and then across and out into Malawi, climbing back on the bicycles, leaving the boy standing by his canoe as we whiz off down the path.

Malawi now, another country. But the same dirt path winding around the bends, the banana trees on the side of the road, the huts half hidden by the leaves, cattle lying six and seven around a smoky fire. Even the same people living here as on the Tanganyikan side, the same tribe, the Nyakusa, who had spilled over the river, no one knows how long ago.

Only now when we pass people along the road and I call *Oogonile* to them, some of them call back *Monile*, not *Oogonile*. Fedson explains that these people are speaking Tumbuka, not Nyakusa, that the Tumbukas are another tribe, the tribe of northern Malawi. There are still many Nyakusa here, he says, but more Tumbuka. And I recall reading somewhere how the Bantu are all related from Somalia to South Africa, that although the tribes are different, al-

147

though they have a different dialect, they are basically the same, the same customs, the same way of life, even the same basic language. And here you can actually see it now, what is the difference between Tanganyika and Malawi except that they are saying *Monile* instead of *Oogonile?*

It seems to be getting hotter now, and I am conscious of being very thirsty, and also very sore from the bumping on the back of the bicycle. The men, the riders, are also growing tired now, they are having difficulty getting up a good speed, so I cannot jump on. And they begin to walk their bicycles so that they can get their strength back.

Then Fedson says that we are approaching Kapolo, and there on the left is a stone building, the first building I can remember seeing today that isn't a mud hut. It is for immigration and customs, he says, we will have to stop there. I look at my watch . . . five o'clock, we have been traveling four hours.

There are two men seated behind a desk and they rise as I enter and begin to look very official. They speak to me in English, demanding my passport and ordering me to open all my luggage. Only one bag? they say, as I bring it in, and one of them walks outside to check if there are any others.

They empty everything out on the desk—toothpaste, soap, shirts, pair of shoes, my one suit that I had spent half an hour folding properly. These idiots!

Then they ask me some questions, about my work, just what am I doing in Tanganyika, and why do I want to come to Malawi. Where am I going after Kapolo, and when, and do I realize that Malawi and Tanganyika are not good friends. No, I don't realize it. What does that have to do with me anyway?

Then they tell me I can put everything back into my suitcase, they haven't found anything. What were they expecting, rifles, grenades perhaps? But they add that I cannot leave Kapolo without notifying them first. I can't understand what all the fuss is about, but I let it go; no sense getting into an argument. Besides I am just too tired, and want to get to Fedson's house where I can sit down and get a drink of water.

Now Fedson points down the road and says that his house is just a little way farther. We pass fields with tall yellow grass, a brick building on the right which says POLICE, more fields and some mud huts set back off the road.

Soon we turn off the road down a dirt path, walking now, the men with the bicycles too tired to carry us. Six little black children run to Fedson, and smile shyly up at him without saying a word. They are his younger brothers and sisters, he tells me, and I wonder how six of them can all be about the same age.

Then three thin worn old women wearing black sacks run up, really shuffling more than running, they are so old—and they are so thin, you can see their bones. They all lie down on the ground, *Oogonile, oogonile, ndaga, ndaga,* as Fedson tells me that these are his mothers, that they are very happy to see us.

His mothers. Mothers! Of course he had told me before, they all had, I had seen Mr. Ngulu's two wives and even Mr. Ndendulu's mothers. But seeing *these* three old women, Fedson's mothers. Fedson, my brightest boy, and hadn't he told me his father was a priest!

They lead us toward a group of little huts, the three old ladies, the six little children, the two riders, Fedson and myself. Four huts all together, with thatched roofs, small, not even the size of ours at Ndumulu, with no doors or windows, only holes cut out where they should be.

Standing in front of them is a little old man, and as I approach, he rushes toward me and grabs my hand in both of his, crying, Welcome, welcome, in English. And then before I can even realize it, the little old man bursts into tears, while I stand there helpless, wondering if I have done anything to offend him, the riders and the mothers and the children and Fedson standing behind me motionless saying nothing.

The old man seems to recover himself and says something to the women, who run off into one of the houses. He goes over to Fedson now and to the two men—*Oogonile, oogonile, ndaga, ndaga.* The women return, each carrying a folding chair, and we sit down, the old man and I and one of the riders in the chairs, Fedson and the other man on the ground, the little children off a little ways.

The old man begins talking in Swahili, shaking his head as he speaks. No, he never would have believed it, a white man coming here, to his house. He never thought it would happen. He had seen British people, all with their cars and fancy clothes, and they would never speak to anyone on the street, never stopping, just passing them without even looking back. Yes, Fedson had written him I was coming, but he hadn't really believed it—that a white man was actually coming to see him, them. They were such poor people, they had nothing.

And listening to him, how can I not be touched? I just want to tell him how happy I am to be able to come and see him, to meet his family, how much I wanted to meet them all, because Fedson is one of the brightest boys I have ever known. (In fact he is so bright that I cannot really imagine his having come from a place like Kapolo. Maybe that is the real reason I wanted to come here, to prove it to myself.)

Now the women come over to us, bringing cups of water, handing one to each of us. I look at the water, all brown and rusty—they couldn't have boiled it—how can I possibly drink it? But I am so thirsty.

And then I think of some pills that I have brought with me that they had given us, just for occasions like this. You can just put them into the water and they are supposed to dissolve, changing the color of the water and purifying it somehow so that it will be safe to drink.

So I ask them whether they mind if I take a pill for myself—medicine—as I am very tired from the journey? I know that I should offer it to them too, as Africans love to take all kinds of medicine. Except that they might become afraid seeing the water change color.

They nod and I take two pills out of my suitcase, they are blue little pellets, very hard, and I put them into my cup, watching them sink to the bottom, just lying there. Well, maybe it takes a while to dissolve.

The two men on the bicycles say they must leave—they want to be back at Kyela before it's too late—as it's nearly six now. I look down into my cup. The pills are still lying there, they haven't made a move.

The men get up to go, touching hands and saying *Mugonege,* goodbye, to all of us—still nothing with those pills.

Goodbye, I say to them—What kind of pills are these? The one time I want to use them they don't work—as they pedal off down the path, and I take a big gulp of water. The hell with it.

So we sit there in front of the house, the old man, Fedson, and I, night just beginning to set in over the fields of tall yellow grass. Now we see Bumi and little Annie coming down the path, Bumi

150

carrying the box on her head as they come up to us and bend down, and I marvel that they have walked nearly as quickly as we have ridden.

Annie sits down with the little brothers and sisters and Bumi off by herself a ways. Then one of the little ones comes and sits next to Bumi, and another one, both staring at her without saying a word, and looking over at us now and then with their big eyes. But quiet, not a sound, they do not want to disturb us as we are talking.

One of the women comes out of the house and says something to Fedson. He tells me that my bath is ready if I want to wash, so I stand up and he leads me back behind the houses and points to a little enclosure, a kind of yard with a fence of wooden planks around it so that no one can see inside. There is a large basin of hot water there on the ground with steam rising, and a cake of soap. I begin taking off my clothes, hanging them on the planks.

Now I straddle the basin and begin splashing myself with the water, hot on my back. And calling to Fedson, Run and bring me my towel from my bag, the water dripping across me as I begin scrubbing with the soap. Fedson handing the towel over the planks so I can reach it, good, scrubbing myself, taking off the heat and the sweat of fifteen miles. That fence around me, the breeze tickling my back, and I cannot help thinking of that first day at Ndumulu, washing outside in the back yard, Africa, a black girl washing herself in the rain, white soapsuds in her black hair.

When I am dry I return to the porch and sit back down with the old man and Fedson, the little children, Annie and Bumi still sitting a little distance away. It is almost dark now, with a little breeze. I look at my watch, seven o'clock.

Do I know that there is an hour's difference between Malawi and Tanganyika? Fedson asks. That it is really six o'clock now, not seven?

And I look across at the countryside, so flat, the fields with the shadows of the tall grass swaying gently in the evening breeze, the quiet. And I can make out some huts off in the distance, and now a man passing on the road. But soon he is gone, and there is nothing now, just the grass waving in the evening stillness. . . . Six o'clock now, not seven—does it really make any difference here?

Then the mosquitoes begin to come. They buzz and sting and crawl under my clothes and into my ears and up my nose, while the old man and Fedson and the little children sit there without even moving or noticing them—an immunity from having lived here all their lives, no doubt.

But seeing me squirming and scratching, they decide we should move inside. So we bring in our chairs, and the floor is hard mud, with a table in the middle of the room, and one of the women brings a hurricane lamp and sets it down on the table.

Soon some people appear in the doorway, three old men with canes, one wearing sandals, the other two barefoot, each with a white sheet draped over his shoulders. They speak to the old man in Nyakusa—or is it Tumbuka?—as Fedson tells me they are his uncles, the old man's brothers, and they have come here to see me, they have heard I have come.

We all smile and greet each other, *Oogonile, oogonile, ndaga, ndaga.* One of them says something to me, and Fedson tells me he is saying that they all have children at school, and I nod my understanding.

Then the wives come into the room, carrying dishes of food on their heads. Rice, chicken, a plate for each of us, another one carries two more chairs, and a spoon for each of us. We begin eating, the old men squeezing the rice into little balls with their hands, while reaching for pieces of chicken to stick in their mouths. So I do the same, squeezing the rice into a little ball as they do, sucking on the soft juicy pieces of chicken.

When we have finished, the wives come and clear off the table, one of them collecting the plates, another sweeping the table clean and the floor, the third walking around to each of us with a bowl of water for us to rinse our hands.

They bring in a pot of tea and put it on the table, and sugar and a tin container of milk. I know the tin is because of me—they can never afford something like this, a tin of milk—and I smile my appreciation to myself. From Ushirika to here, they are all the same, always sharing with us however little they have, always giving us the best that they can possibly afford, like the Leek's offering us his month's supply of meat at his house.

The old men sit there slurping their tea out of their cups, the lamp burning low, the smell of food hanging in the air, the drone of an occasional mosquito. Then they are talking softly among themselves, almost whispering, and Fedson tells me that they would like to hear about America. Would I tell them something?

152

So I begin, talking in Swahili, very slowly, to think of what I will say next—What would they be interested in hearing? What can I say that they will understand?

America is a big country, very big, much bigger than Tanganyika or Malawi, its cities with big buildings, the skyscrapers, the crops that we grow—with Fedson giving a running translation into Nyakusa to one of the men, who does not speak Swahili, as they all nod their heads.

Then one of them asks if when it is day in Africa, it is night in America. One of their children learned that in school, and they wonder whether it is really true. So I explain to them, as best I can in Swahili, Yes, it really is, making Fedson the sun and myself the earth, the way I showed the boys in class, revolving and rotating around the sun, my face Africa, my back America, showing how when I face the sun, it is day and when my back is to the sun, it is night, and that one complete rotation is twenty-four hours or one day. They sit there enthralled, these four old men, their eyes staring at me, their mouths open, nodding their heads as I walk around Fedson, turning my body in rotation, not sure whether it is because they really understand or whether they just like seeing me walking in circles.

And watching them I realize that this must be what happens all over Africa when the children come home from school, the parents sitting around just like these old men, asking them what they had learned at school this year, and Fedson or whoever he is telling them all the new things night after night. Maybe about geography, mountains, deserts or snow. Or circles, triangles, maybe even multiplying or adding. And I can just picture all these old men all over Africa nodding their heads, smiling in fascination night after night, just like listening to a great fairy tale.

Then one of the uncles asks me, When the earth revolves around the sun, will it come back to the same place? Yes, I say.

And if it takes one day to make one rotation, how many days will it take the earth to go all the way around the sun to the same place?

Three hundred and sixty-five days, I say.

Then, says the old man, does that mean that when the sun is back in the same place, it is *mwaka moja,* one year?

And I look at him, this man who I was sure could not read, who hadn't been to school one day in his life, and who had yet understood in one minute what it takes people God knows how long to understand.

Yes, I say, that's exactly it, my voice a little excited, and he nods his head and begins explaining it to the others, pointing to me as the sun and standing up and revolving around me, trying to explain to them what it means when the earth completes a full revolution. They nod their heads, the other old men, but I don't think they understand the way he does.

Now they begin talking to each other, their voices rising and falling with the lilt of their language. One of the uncles is speaking now, very slowly, nodding his head, making waving motions with his hands. He is speaking Nyakusa now, as Fedson translates into English for me. He is telling about a journey he made last month, he was near Blantyre and the bus broke down, and they had to stay inside the bus and wait twenty-four hours until another bus passed to take them. And it is the way he says it—the bus broke down and we had to stay there—so matter-of-fact, there was no alternative, as if what else was there to do?

And I cannot help thinking how angry I always became whenever the bus we were on—Mike and I—broke down. Angry not so much at the bus's breaking down but at the people, who would just get out their food and blankets for the night, as though they didn't really mind, just accepting it as though there was nothing else to do.

Yet listening to this old man now, how can I be angry at him, what can I possibly expect from him? He is just an ignorant old man. What else could he have done, what else is there for them to do when the bus breaks down? And I realize that this old man is no different from any of the passengers I've traveled with. What do they know, these people? What have I expected of them? Could they wave down the first European that passed? Do I really think anyone passing would have stopped for them?

Suddenly I catch myself yawning.

Would I like to go to sleep now? Fedson asks. Maybe I am tired from the journey, as we have come a long way.

All right, I think, I am tired. So I get up and say my good-nights to the old men, *Ndaga, ndaga* shaking hands with each of them as Fedson leads me into one of the other rooms. Inside there are two beds, made from planks of wood. No mattress, only a blanket thrown across the planks, to serve as a sheet, I guess.

Fedson points to the bed with a hole cut out of the mud wall above it for a window. I am to sleep there because it is open, he says. He will sleep in the other bed, and he takes down a mosquito net hanging on the wall, apologizing that it has a hole in it, as he sticks his arm through the hole all the way to his shoulder to show me—as if I do not believe him.

I am not sure whether to use the blanket as a sheet and sleep without a blanket covering, or to sleep right on top of the planks under the blanket, so I begin playing with the buttons of my shirt as Fedson goes out into the other room. I hear his voice, and I have my shirt almost unbuttoned when Bumi walks in, her young brown body gliding across the light in the doorway—she must be about fifteen or sixteen—holding a blanket over her arm, and she walks to the bed and unfolds it over the blanket which is already there.

She smiles as she walks out, and I take off my pants and slide myself between the blankets and the mosquito net, which hangs over me like a giant spider web with the great hole in the middle. I am very tired and the planks are very hard. And I listen to the voices in the other room, the rise and fall, the lilt of the Nyakusa— or is it Tumbuka?—the dim light of the hurricane lamp, the light becoming dimmer, the voices farther and farther away.

Then it is all dark and Fedson is in the other bed—I haven't heard him come in, not that I can see him either, but I can hear the rise and fall of his breathing. Unconsciously I am scratching my-self, and listening to the dive-bomber noises of the mosquitoes as they circle in on me. I try to turn over onto my back, except my arm is caught somewhere between me and the planks. And even on my back it is still hard. And the buzzing, and every now and then I get one, wiping it and its blood off my hand onto the edge of the wooden bed.

But they are hitting me all over now, and I am trying to turn in the bed but I ache all over—damn those planks—while Fedson breathes as calmly and easily as a little baby, occasionally clouting his face in his sleep, then turning over without even waking up. Those people, how can they do it?

Later I hear a rooster crowing, and another one answering him. Still dark but I have slept some, as they crow back and forth to each other. Who was the joker who said that roosters crow only at dawn? Maybe he did not mean African roosters.

Later a shred of light through the window-hole. I look at my watch. Five o'clock. Fedson still sleeping. Well, this is about as much as I can take for a night. So I lift up the net and put my feet down on the floor—cold now because of the night—and slip by Fedson, and into my pants, out through the middle room.

Outside there against the house are the little children—ten of them, sleeping outdoors, each on his own mat—curled up like little balls, their bodies breathing ever so gently, like black baby angels. I stand above and peer down at them. I don't want to come too close and disturb them, there is almost something holy about their sleeping there so calmly, so peacefully together.

I slip past them now behind the house to a little hut near where I bathed last night. Inside there is a mound of dirt with a hole in the middle, and of course I don't have any toilet paper—they would probably laugh at me if they knew I used it.

Then back into the house, fumbling with my suitcase, when I hear a baby crying outside. Now another one, the sound of stretching and yawns, Fedson opening his eyes now and lifting himself out of bed, the pitter-patter of feet in the next room, their little world has awakened.

Fedson stands up now and puts on his clothes, his shorts and a shirt—the same clothes he wears at school, probably the only ones he owns. Outside Bumi has a bowl of hot water, and as she flicks out a piece of soap from inside her dress and hands it to me, I can't help thinking of Mrs. Twakatulu flicking out her breast.

I begin to wash, Bumi holding the bowl, hot, as it burns my hands and I make a face. She laughs, a pretty little laugh. In a few years, maybe sooner, will she be flicking her breast out just as she had the soap, like Mrs. Twakatulu and all the other wives?

The old man comes in and we sit around the table and the women bring us hot tea with bread, which I know they would never eat unless there was a special guest, as bread is so costly. And milk from that tin. How kind of them it all is.

When we finish, the women begin cleaning off the table and sweeping out the room. It seems so remarkable the way they work together, no jealousy, almost like a team. As though sharing a husband is not half bad.

Then Fedson says that he wants to show me the lake. So we set off, crossing the main road that we had come on yesterday, and cut down a small path past some mud huts. Everyone seems to be just waking up now, chickens walking around the road, little children

156

around the house, with people passing us, old women, cloths wrapped around their little bodies, great baskets on their heads, and wrinkled old men who call *Monile* to us in chorus, *Monile, monile*.

The road has turned to sand with fields on either side. It is all so flat, only those fields, the tall yellow grass stretching as far as the eye can see. And there through the tall grass I can see the lake. But it is not the lake that I have seen from Tanganyika all those times, not the sparkling, shiny blue, but rather a somber gray, sullen, almost dirty black.

I take off my shoes now, walking barefoot across the sand in the early morning, as we approach the shore. There is a line of small rowboats beached, and some people standing near who stare at us as we pass, and some little boys who begin following us across the sand down toward the water's edge.

Let's swim, I say to Fedson, and we take off our clothes, and leave them on the beach as the little boys creep closer to stare at my white body. I smile reassuringly to myself, I must be the first white man they have ever seen, but I am happy to run into the safety of the water as the little boys follow us to the water's edge.

I begin doing a breaststroke out to where the water is over my head, and then I lie on my back and look up at the sun, feeling very cool and calm in the early morning water. The little boys jump into the water now, waving their arms about and swimming toward me like a school of fish. They are imitating my breaststroke, splashing about, calling out to each other so that I will look at them.

I cannot help smiling to myself—kids, they're all the same when they're kids—and I decide this might be the best time to make my escape from their staring. So I swim back to the shore and lie down on the sand, naked, on my stomach, as the sun gently licks my back.

Later we swim again, then dress, and begin walking back, the little children following us at a safe distance. Fedson says he wants to show me the new school they are building, so we cut off the sand road through someone's field—and I feel as though I am trespassing through someone's garden—and there is the school, half finished, of brick. It will have a thatched roof, Fedson says, because there isn't enough money to buy corrugated tin.

Soon we are back at Fedson's home. One wife brings chairs for us and another wife brings some mangoes for me which she has already peeled and sliced. Fedson points to a tree near us, this is where the mangoes come from. A mango tree in his own back yard. Another wife brings us tea, and I am feeling very comfortable and very tired—good tired—from the swim and the long walk, and it is ten o'clock already and becoming hot.

We pull our chairs under the mango tree where it is shady, and the old man joins us and we sit together. Soon a young boy rides up the path on a bicycle, and Fedson gets up to greet him. He comes over to me, we touch hands, *Oogonile, oogonile, ndaga, ndaga,* and to the old man, *Oogonile, oogonile, ndaga, ndaga.* Fedson tells me that he was a classmate of this boy last year, but that the boy did not have enough money for his school fees this year.

They sit and talk for a while, speaking to each other in Nyakusa, Fedson and his friend, and I cannot understand what they are saying, and the sun is climbing higher in the sky and the wind has ceased. And even in the shade now it is very hot, the high yellow grass standing there in the fields without a motion.

Soon Fedson's friend gets up and leaves, pedaling his bicycle along the path, turning into the road and fading off behind the fields. I want to take a book from my bag because how long can you just sit? But I think that they might be offended. And it occurs to me, what will Fedson do here during his holiday? Will you sit here like this day after day, doing nothing?

Yes, he says, that is what he will do.

But won't you get tired? I mean sitting here with nothing to do? Because the holiday is two months. Two months of sitting, of doing nothing day after day.

No, he says, he won't get tired. He is used to it. He has been doing it all his life.

As he is talking, I hear a noise in the distance, a hum, the sound of a motor. I look up and two great green trucks are passing on the road. The back of the trucks all packed with villagers, old men half naked in half-torn clothes, one on top of the other, arms and legs and toes sticking out helter-skelter. The old man sees them and stands up, waving to them as they pass. Karonga, he tells me in Swahili. They are going to Karonga. Dr. Banda, the Prime Minister, is there. They are going to the rally for him at Karonga.

Then I see three old men walking down the path toward us. The uncles from last night. They live close by, Fedson tells me.

*Oogonile, ndaga, oogonile, ndaga,* to each of us, and one wife brings out some chairs for them as they join us under the tree. Another brings a bowl of pombe, which she places on the ground at our feet, and we begin to drink. They pass me the bowl as I take a sip, speaking to each other now, their voices rising and falling as I glance at my watch. Nearly eleven o'clock, the sun rising higher in the sky.

And sitting there, watching these men drinking—Fedson doesn't drink because he is still a schoolboy—and looking out at the tall yellow fields, flat, bare, I feel as though I have really come to the end of the world. And not just the end, the beginning as well, where yesterday is today and today is tomorrow, where all the todays are the same as all the yesterdays and all the tomorrows. Where life doesn't seem to have changed since the beginning of time, and where it doesn't seem that it will ever change until the end of time. Where life seems to have gone on for generations and generations, for hundreds, for maybe thousands, of years, waking up to a rooster's crowing or a baby's crying, going to sleep with the mosquitoes, the wives cooking, the men sitting there drinking, planting during the planting season, which begins two months before the rains, then sitting inside their huts when the rains come, which last another two months, and then harvesting for two months during the harvesting season which follows the rains. And that takes care of six months of the year, but what do they do for the rest of the time, when there is no harvesting or planting, day after day, month after month, year after year, generation after generation, century after century?

And sitting there looking out at the fields that stretch for miles and miles, the tall yellow grass that stands motionless now in the midday sun—it suddenly comes to me, the great answer, the why. Why my students, why the teachers, are the way they are, why they all are the way they are, why everything is the way it is. And the answer begins right here in Kapolo.

Why the boys have so much trouble in math, why it is that they know nothing, why they have no background. Coming from these villages—how many Kapolos must there be where they haven't seen anything except these fields day after day?

And even those who go to the little school with the thatched roof that they are building, how can they learn to multiply if the teacher doesn't know how himself? For how many Mr. Mwadundas must there be, all over Africa, teachers who teach Standard 6 but don't

159

know triangles or rectangles? And what happens if the child is sick, when the class is learning borrowing for subtraction, what does he do then? Can he go home and ask his father, an ignorant old man, who doesn't know how to read, who knows even less about subtraction than the child?

So he might go on, maybe missing borrowing here, maybe multiplying later on, and then on to fractions, but how can you do decimals without knowing how to do fractions? Until by the time he has a choice, if he has somehow managed to pass his exam, he will choose history or politics, because he has never learned any math. Or he may become a teacher, teaching math to other little children just the way he himself has been taught.

Or graphs. Can I really be surprised now that they had so much trouble? That they couldn't tell time? When had they ever needed to tell time? Six o'clock in Malawi, seven o'clock in Tanganyika—what did that mean to them? What can a graph possibly mean to them? When had they ever in their lives seen anything resembling a graph, how old were they before they first saw a book, when was the first time they had gone outside their village?

And it is not just the schoolboys, it is everything, life, their whole way of life, their way of doing things. The political rallies, packing those villagers in the trucks, taking them to Karonga to hear Dr. Banda. Maybe he was going to swagger about and scream American spies. Why did they all swagger about? I can begin to understand it now, because they know nothing else, because they come from nothing, from a place like Kapolo, where all they know is the fields.

Or the teachers at school, can I wonder why they didn't want us at their meeting? Can I really wonder now why they didn't accept us as part of them? Because how different from them we really are, from them who have all grown up drinking dirty water, never wearing shoes, who have had three mothers like Fedson, who are immune to the mosquitoes, to dirty water, who are used to sitting there drinking pombe day after day, drinking from morning until night—it is all a way of life for them, because there is nothing else for them to do. And seeing it here in Kapolo, admitting it now to myself for the first time, what really do we have in common with these people? That we speak a little Swahili, or a few words of Nyakusa, that we sip pombe with them twice a week—detesting the smell and the

160

taste and everything else about it—that we eat at their houses occasionally, always afraid that we may become sick?

What really do we have in common with these people? Is there any reason for them to accept us? Because we are not of them. How can we possibly think for a minute that we are? No wonder they treated us like an adornment, as something to be worn around the neck to show their friends. How could they believe seriously that we were part of them? These ignorant, uneducated villagers . . . they have been more sensible, more honest, about accepting us or not accepting us, than we have been.

But yet whatever differences do exist, through it all you can feel a basic goodness and warmth and kindness about these people, which almost seems more important than whatever differences there are. From that first day we arrived at Ndumulu—their tea party, the old man along the road to Ushirika thanking us for having come here to help Tanganyika, calling *Isaga* to us, welcome to their bowls, Medson and the officers inviting us to their homes, the Leek's being so pleased every time we came to his hut, the way he always tried to give us meat, poor as he was. Or the bus driver not letting us pay, thanking us for having come here to Tanganyika to help them, the Twak trying to feed me meat every night, his way of thanking me. Old man Mwandemele here at Kapolo, crying like that when I came, giving me milk, bread, apologizing for being poor, and yet giving me all he had, things that were so dear to him.

Yes, they had their own culture, their own values, these people. Backward, primitive maybe, with ignorance and magic, yes, but was it really all so bad?

Were they with their magic so different from these Christians, these missionaries who were coming here trying to change them? Missionaries like Rod and Rolene, with their servants and their five little blond children who had probably never played with an African child in their whole lives—missionaries like these, who have the nerve to tell the African he must have only one wife, he can't get to heaven if he has more than one. What is wrong with an African having more than one wife? That's what I want to know. It seemed to work out fine for them, they all seemed contented. Who are we to tell them anything different?

Suddenly I hear a car door slam and two men in khaki trousers are stepping out of a Land Rover and walking toward us. They greet all the old men, *Monile, monile,* and me in English, Good afternoon. And they drink from the bowl and pass it around, and I assume they all know everybody and that they have merely come to visit. Fedson tells me that they are local police officers, and they begin to ask me, speaking in English, where I have come from and what I am doing in Malawi.

I tell them I am here to visit Fedson and his family, planning to go on to Karonga tomorrow. And how long will I be staying in Karonga?

I explain to them that I am just passing through, I am going south.

They smile and I smile, and I think that it is very nice of them to come here like this. Soon they go off, and we see clouds of dust behind their Land Rover. The sun is on the downward arc now, and a little breeze springs up, and the tall grass ripples in the wind.

In the evening the men from customs and immigration appear at the house to tell me that I will not be allowed to proceed to Karonga tomorrow. Dr. Banda is there. And they are not certain that I am not a spy. They must stop all foreigners who cross from Tanganyika, owing to the dispute. I may have a weapon on me, they say, I may want to go to Karonga to kill Dr. Banda.

I tell them that they have already searched me and questioned me, and I have told them who I am and what I am doing, and that they have seen my passport. What more can they need?

But they shake their heads, they cannot be sure, I must wait here until Dr. Banda has left Karonga.

How long will that be?

Four or five days. They are not sure.

But I can't stay here four or five days—thinking of that bed and the mosquitoes.

You must, they say. If I do go anyplace, I will be seized by the Youth League bands as they know my description. That was why the two police officers came. Now they have gone to Karonga to give my description to the bands. My description?

I realize that it won't do any good to argue. I can prove to them conclusively that I am not a spy, and it still won't do any good. My description. It is mad. But I also know I am not going to stay here any four days. And I also know about the Malawi Youth League bands.

They stalk off and the old men make clucking noises with their tongues in sympathy. It's too bad, they say, very bad. And I can't help smiling at them, they mean well, dammit, they just don't know. I nod to them to say I appreciate their commiseration, but my mind is working, I am waiting for the night.

Night in the house, with its stuffiness, just the little lamp burning, the drone of an occasional mosquito. The old women are cleaning off the table where we have just finished eating, and we are sitting on chairs against the wall. The three uncles are still there, they are drinking another bowl of pombe. My bites are bothering me, I am constantly scratching. It is already worse than last night.

I have been thinking of what to do, and now I go into my overnight bag and take an unworn sleeveless sweater which was given to me as a gift, and present it to the old man. I announce that I want to give this sweater to him as a way of thanking him. And they all smile as the old man runs his fingers up and down through the wool, he has never seen anything like it. And he gives it to the uncles, who fondle it and nod their heads appreciatively, Oooh, ahha.

Suddenly the old man is lying there on the floor with his hand stuck out at me, crying, Thank you, thank you, in English. The poor old man—this is not what I wanted. Yet there is something very moving, very touching, in it, although it is almost ludicrous his saying, Thank you, thank you, in English.

Then I say to them that I am leaving in the middle of the night, at three A.M., back to Tanganyika, that I want Fedson to come with me to show me the way, and I say it all in one quick sentence as they sit there, as if stunned.

Then the old man asks, What about the Youth League boys? And I say, That is why we are leaving in the middle of the night at three A.M. when everyone will be sleeping, because I think we can make the border by daylight.

They are afraid, so I tell them they can just say I left by myself in case they are asked, and besides nothing can happen because I have done nothing, they will soon realize that I am not a spy. And I tell them how important this is since I have a long way to go

163

south—especially now as I must go back to Tanganyika to start again.

The old man begins apologizing, How sorry he is that I can't stay longer, and I say, Yes, I would like to, I should be happy to, except that I cannot wait four days. Of course I could never stay here four days at all—not because I'd be late but because I'd die of mosquito bites and lack of sleep from that bed.

So it seems agreed, I will go, and the old man says they will all escort me part way, but I tell them, No, it is not necessary for the uncles to come, as they live a mile or so away.

All right, he says, but that he and Bumi will walk a little way and Fedson will go the rest of the distance with me.

Good, and I tell them I want to get to sleep, it is almost ten o'clock now, and I go around and say my final goodbyes to the uncles.

Then lying down, and the bed is just as hard as last night, and the hole in the mosquito net is just as large, and I can hear the old men outside in the room, their voices the only sound, rising and falling, getting softer and falling way. The first mosquito bites me and I pull the blanket up over my head, but it is not long enough, my toes are sticking out, and I try to shift positions but ouch . . . those damn planks. And there is another mosquito stinging my face. Slap. I feel it in my hand and flick it on the floor. Let that serve as a warning to the rest of them. And I look at my watch to see how much longer until three o'clock.

But I do sleep and when I do wake up, I glance at my watch, it is nearly four and quick I call to Fedson to get up and call the rest of them, we are late. He gets up without a word and goes out of the room as I stumble into my pants, hearing the sounds of people moving about.

I come into the room, the mothers are all there, one of them holding a lantern they have lit, and the old man walks in as the women hand Fedson a loaf of bread for the trip. He asks me if they should make some tea, but No, we are late already and we begin saying goodbye, *Ndaga fidyo, ookagone, oogonege,* as Bumi enters, Ready.

I finish my goodbyes by the small light and walk outside, and it is refreshingly cool with a full moon, very bright and round, shining on the fields. And the little children sleeping, each on his own mat, against the side of the house, the little black angels.

We tiptoe past them, down the path to the road, the moon shining on the furrows, past the police station as I look at my watch. Four-thirty. We are late. And I was hoping to make the border before sunrise, when the policemen inside would be waking up.

The road ends and we cut across a little footpath, the four of us, Fedson first, then the old man and Bumi, and I. Fifteen miles and this is just the beginning. An old woman passes us and they all greet her, *Monile, monile.* Fedson says she has come from Kyela— which means she has been walking all night—a little, old lady like that and I wonder where she is going, what is so important in her life that she has to walk all night?

The path turns sharply, to the left again, and it occurs to me that this is not the path we came on. No, Fedson says, that it is shorter without the bicycles, we will be crossing the Songwe farther upstream. Soon the old man calls to us to stop. He says that we have come a mile, and that he and Bumi will go back. I shake hands with him and he smiles, the moonlight on his face, his toothless gums. He looks very happy, although he begins apologizing to me again, Next time everything will be better.

Bumi kneels down and says her goodbyes, and I feel like popping a big kiss on her forehead. I wonder what will happen to her now as Fedson tells me she has failed her exams. What is there for her to do now but stay at home and get married? And I think of her living here the rest of her life, weaving mats every day, married to someone like Mr. Mwambigila or Mr. Ngubile or Fedson's friend who came on the bicycle.

Now Fedson is leading, the path stretching in long curves, the moon shining down on us, two of us now, on and on into the night. We can see people coming toward us, coming from Kyela like the little old lady, as we call out to them, *Monile.* But I am afraid that if the policemen look for us they will be asking these people as they come into Kapolo whether they have seen us.

Soon there on the right are some streaks of light, and I look at my watch, it's after five and the morning is coming. And suddenly there is a flash of light behind us, like nothing I've ever seen before, like the light that comes from a firecracker, except that it fills the whole sky. My first thought is, My God, they're firing flares after me, but that's crazy, and Fedson says that it is lightning, a storm is coming—the first rains of the season—of all days for it to begin. If only we can make the border before the rain.

The day is coming up, and the flashes seem to be following us. But it's still a long way off, and now you can see it's lightning as we cut to another path to the right. The storm seems to be running parallel to us now, not coming any nearer, maybe we will miss it. But now we cut back to the left and it is lightning all right, and the day doesn't seem to be getting any brighter. Fedson says it's going to hit soon, but I say, No, it can't be more than three miles to the border, let's keep going.

But then the storm does hit, hard, that first rain all right, making up for all the dry season, as we run toward the nearest hut. There is an old woman outside, she looks as if she has just gotten up. *Isaga,* she says, leading us inside. She brings me a chair to sit on, and Fedson puts my bag down on the floor. Another old woman comes into the room, carrying a baby on her back, and she comes near me and kneels down as we touch hands. I see the baby is awake and I smile at it and it looks at me and begins to scream. And suddenly two little children, who are also in the hut, who have been staring at me, also begin to scream, as the first old woman shoos them into a corner and the second—the one with the baby—pulls out some kind of food from between her breasts and sticks it into the baby's mouth.

An old man enters and speaks to me in Nyakusa. When he sees I do not understand, he speaks to Fedson, who translates into English. He wants to know who I am, where I am from, and where I am going, and Fedson answers him. He says something to the second woman, who goes out into the rain—across to another hut. Soon she comes back with a pot of tea and some cups.

She pours the tea and the old man pulls some sugar out of somewhere. I smile without realizing it, it is such a kind, warm gesture, and I get that feeling in my stomach when nice things like this happen to me, but I also keep peeping outside to see if it's getting any lighter and if there are any police, because they must be up by now, and it's only a question of whether they have any sense, and how hard they want to do their job. Surely they don't like walking in the rain any more than I do.

Finally though the rain seems to be quieter so I nudge Fedson, *Ndaga* to the old man, wishing there is something I can give him for his kindness. I tell Fedson to write down the old man's address, I will write him a letter—Swahili people love to receive letters.

He breaks into a great smile as Fedson tells him this, and I take

166

a paper and pen out of my bag. He tells Fedson to write, as he himself doesn't know how. Then goodbye to the two ladies, and we are off again with me looking over my shoulder every now and then to see if anyone is after me.

But it's O.K. now, I feel they are not coming, they had their chance when we were stuck at the house, and soon we are approaching the Songwe. But there is no boy with a canoe as we are crossing farther upstream. And instead of going right across Fedson is walking along the bank, looking for a place where it is not too deep.

I tell him, Come on, just let's cross, even though I know there is Bilharzia disease there. But at the moment nothing can be worse than another night at Fedson's with those mosquitoes and that bed. And I am half walking backward as I am speaking, ready to charge right into the water and start swimming, bag and all, should I see anybody resembling a policeman or a Youth League boy.

Fedson keeps on walking as though he doesn't hear me as the Songwe curves on and on. Now he says he has found a place where he doesn't think it is too deep—thank God—and we begin descending the little hill down to the riverbank. It seems pretty deep out there in the middle, and I guess it's nearly over our heads, and I take a long look at the water—brown and stagnant because the rains haven't begun yet—and I wonder what is in it besides Bilharzia as we take our shoes off, or at least I do because Fedson is barefoot anyway.

I take my trousers off—Fedson is wearing shorts. He goes in first with my bag on his head as the water comes up only to the beginning of his shorts.

Then I go in, in my underwear. Now I'm in the middle and the water is brown but cool, and then I've done it, I'm over the worst, and I am coming out at the other side. And there is a crowd of people who have suddenly gathered from out of nowhere to watch us, to see the great *Mzungu,* and as I'm not wearing any trousers I go behind a big rock to put them on. They think this is very funny and get a big laugh out of it—ha-ha—and then we're on our way again, cutting in between rows of banana trees, their rain-drenched leaves dripping on us. But it doesn't matter now because I'm on the other side, the Tanganyikan side. I never realized I could ever feel this good about being back in Tanganyika.

Then that great field, and I am beginning to feel very tired now, it seems to stretch as far as I can see and I look back every now and then to make sure that we are really moving. And now we are meeting more people on the path, people coming from Kyela. I look at my watch, nine o'clock, Tanganyikan time, which means that we have been going about four hours. If we hurry I can make the one o'clock bus to Mbeya. Then we are in the middle of the field, flatness stretching all about us, the sky still gray, it looks as though it is going to rain again.

Now the trees are coming up, we are getting nearer to the other side of the field, and we cut through those big banana leaves again. Then there is the dirt road, the bicycle road that we came on, it doesn't seem as though it was only two days ago.

Then the rains come, swooshing down on us again, and we head for the first hut we can see. It has a porch so we run underneath it, and a lady comes out and looks hard at me and says *Isaga,* as a little boy comes out in a white shirt and shorts. And it is Asumwike Mwambatula, one of my students—I'll be a son of a gun—and he bursts out into a wide grin as his whole family suddenly pours out onto the porch. Seeing us there, smiling at each other, they all begin to laugh—*oogoniles* and *ndagas*—as they bring some chairs for us to sit on.

Fedson begins to tell them about our journey and where I have been. I ask Asumwike in English how he is enjoying his holiday at home, and he says, Fine, and tells his family what I have said, and they all laugh. Then they bring out towels for us to dry ourselves and cups of tea and bread, and how nice it all is, sitting there on the porch, the rain pouring down, the sky a real American November gray.

Suddenly I hear a noise and quick I perk up; it sounds like a car. I run out onto the road in the rain, and sure enough a truck is coming, and I begin waving it down. The driver stops. He's an Indian and he's going to Kyela and from there on to Mbeya, and, yes, he will take me.

I scream for my bag. Fedson runs out with it and throws it on the truck as I run back to say my goodbyes to the family, standing there in the rain now, saying a final goodbye to Fedson.

Then I'm in the truck and we're moving, the rain tearing down outside, and I think how right everything is, the way it is when you've been waiting a long time for a ride and finally it comes. And suddenly it occurs to me what I will do, I will go to Mbeya, and then to Dar es Salaam and fly right to Salisbury, and start hitchhiking south from there. And they will all be there in Mbeya at Kim Buck's house, Mike and the boys, playing poker. How surprised they will be, opening up the door and seeing me, Mike speechless, startled, and I saying, Gentlemen, move over, I've come a long way for this game.

# PART TWO

# IV

YOU COULD TELL IT was Rhodesia, white man's country, just by
looking down at the land. Because before where it had been brown
scrub with some huts, or forest where all you could see was the
outlines of trees with sometimes a pencil-thin line of dirt road, now
it was farmland, rich, rolling, long, sleek lines of furrows, green
and straight, with fresh brick houses, their tin roofs glistening in the
sunlight, and a road, tarmac, black and clear, gleaming like silver.

Salisbury. It was raining when we landed, late afternoon and
gray skies, whisked into the terminal building, white customs officials, white faces with blond hair, dressed in long white socks, white
shorts and white shirts. I wondered whether I would have any difficulty what with coming from Tanganyika, but no, just a hasty
glance at my passport, a nod, and outside to a taxi, a big, black
limousine.

I wasn't sure where to go, but the African driver held open the
door and said, Yes, baas, as if he expected me to know where I was
going, and I scrambled into the back seat out of the rain. Some
good hotel, I said. I wanted to enjoy myself here.

Yes, baas, he said as we swished down the rainy streets, rain
splashing on the windshield, past other cars with white drivers,
wide streets and big buildings.

He stopped outside a hotel, and the doorman, another African,
whisked my bag inside. THE AMBASSADOR, the sign said, and it was
expensive all right—sixty-five shillings for a single. The man at the
desk, a white man, called to another African, Hey, boy, take the
baas's bag. The African ran over, not really running, as he was

only a few feet away, but rather moving his legs with exaggerated motions—to show how enthusiastic he was, I guess.

My room was small but somehow they had managed to squeeze in an air conditioner, a dresser, a desk and a double bed. And in the bathroom a shower and a bath with running water, hot and cold, so I took off my clothes and into the shower first thing. Was there ever a man who appreciated a good shower more than I?

Later I decided I'd like to see some of the night life, so I put on my suit that I had folded so carefully in my bag and walked outside toward the tallest buildings, where everything was all lit up. The rain had stopped but the pavement was still sleek, with puddles and blurred wet lights and night coming on. Ahead was a park, all lit up, with a Christmas tree and Santa Claus figures. Christmas, not even a month away. So strange it seemed, Christmas in Rhodesia. It was warm, it was not winter, it was summertime. What was Christmas in the summertime?

I wandered around a bit, had some supper, and later I found a place, up a flight of stairs, down to the end of a hallway, through two push doors, into a little dark room. Sounds of a band and loud talking, a small stage in the center with a dance floor, some little tables set back against the far corner where it was darkest, just a little candle flickering on each table.

To the right was the bar. I climbed onto a stool and ordered a beer, and turned around to see the couples dancing, they were all getting up from their tables now, young, maybe in their twenties, they looked like boys out with their dates.

Soon the band cleared away and the couples went back to their tables. And two girls walked out, one tall, the other short, the tall one very ugly. They began to sing, the tall one singing the bass, and could she sing, deep and throaty—you could almost forget how ugly she was. They sang a couple of fast ones, and some slow ones, with more people coming into the bar now, all white people making a lot of noise. The place was filling up, but you could still hear the two girls; they were singing "Make Yourself Comfortable, Baby," and it sounded great the way they did it, that double voice, as I leaned back on my stool and had another beer.

Then a man weaved against my stool and started talking to me, and we agreed the two girls were damn good. And hearing me speak he said, Hey, you're a Yank. As I nodded my head, he called over to somebody, Hey Marv, Poppy, there's a Yank here.

Two men came over, big, and stood around my stool, as the first one pointed at me, and they smiled. So you're a Yank, huh. How do you like Rhodesia? And as I was sipping my beer, I nodded my head until I was finished swallowing, and then said I had arrived just today but that I liked what I had seen—pointing to those two girls.

Look, they said, why don't you come around with us tonight, we'll show you the town. And the first one said, Great place, Rhodesia, we've got everything here—except too many Kaffirs, and I said, What? And he said, Hey now, you don't like the bloody Kaffirs do you? You're not one of those who have come here to help them, are you? And I said, What's a Kaffir? And he said, Oh, what do you call them in America? And the second one said, Nigger, yeah, nigger, that's what they call them, and the first one said, Yeah, too many bloody Kaffirs.

Then they introduced themselves—Marv and Poppy. And the first one Charles—not Charlie. Charles. Poppy said that they were all tobacco farmers about 150 miles east of Salisbury and that they had all come in today to celebrate Marv's new baby as his wife had given birth just this morning. They had been here drinking since twelve this afternoon they said, as Poppy ordered another round and we all drank to Marv's newborn baby. And Poppy said that Marv was one of the best in the world, he had worked for Marv for seven years, but now he was on his own, he had bought his own farm right next to Marv's, that's the way it was here in Rhodesia, a need and a chance for every man that was willing and able to work. He himself had come from South Africa seven years ago, he was thirty now, and look at him, with his own farm.

We're going to show you some really good places, he said to me, they had them here in Salisbury, it was a great city—not like New York, of course, and he winked at me, By the way, where are you from?

New York, I said, and he called out to the other two who were looking over at the girls, Hey, he's from New York, and they all said, Well, this Salisbury is no New York, but it's a great place all the same, there are some great things here in Salisbury, everything that we need anyway.

So we drank to Salisbury and I let them lead me out to the car, and Marv said we weren't missing anything here anyway as the girls were finished until after one. Besides, there were better places.

Then we were at another place, this time down a flight of stairs, and Poppy told me not to say anything, just to walk in right behind them, as it was a kind of private club, but they would take care of everything by telling them that I was a Yank.

Yes, said Marv, everyone here likes Yanks, and he wanted me to know how really sorry he was, how really sorry they all were when Kennedy died. Not that he or the country here agreed with all his ideas. They didn't. But they all knew what a fine man he was and what he stood for and what a great loss it was.

Yes, I said, it's true, thank you—funny how you can say thank you about that, as though he were a member of your family.

Then Poppy was introducing me to the bouncer, and then the manager. What did I think of Rhodesia? they all wanted to know, and I said it looked pretty good so far. And standing at the bar, very dark, with everybody pushing and jostling everybody, as Marv bought another round, I noticed that Charles must be really drunk, because he was going around to the tables, pinching some women on their rears. Then suddenly a man grabbed him, it was his date that Charles had just pinched, and then even more suddenly Marv and Poppy were grabbing the man, and Marv floored him with a right, sending him sprawling between the tables, and he lay there unconscious, his date kneeling over him, looking as though she were going to cry.

Then the three of them, Marv, Poppy and Charles, strolled back to the bar and ordered another round, introducing me to more of their friends as though things like this happened two or three times a night. And all the friends wanted to know what I thought of Rhodesia, and I told them I couldn't complain so far, and then Marv said, Hey, the show must be starting now. So we drank up and I followed them into another room, full of people seated at tables, and we sat down at one as another bouncer came over to see our tickets or something, but Marv explained that I was a Yank and somehow that seemed to do because we all shook hands and he went away.

Soon a blonde wearing only a mink coat and high heels came out and started wiggling her way through the tables up to the front of the room, as they all called out to her, Hey, Queenie, tugging at her mink. But she managed to slip away from all of them, and as she passed our table Charles said to her very softly, Hey, Queenie, and she stopped for a second, and suddenly he screamed out, Hey,

176

Queenie, you don't even got a cunt, you're a bloody man, and we all burst out laughing at that, even me—I guess I must have been a little drunk myself—and she stuck her face up to his and said, Oh yeah, wanna bet? And he said, Yeah, and pulled out a twenty-pound note from his pocket and waved it in her face, as the room rocked with cheers and laughter.

Yeah, Charles said, I got twenty pounds that says you're a man, and the other tables burst into applause. And she said very calmly, Just give it to me, hey, and we'll see, and she called out, Any other takers? With Marv and Poppy egging Charles on, pounding him on the back as he was still holding the money, everyone in the place applauding and hollering and cheering, but I didn't see anyone else going for his wallet.

Then she said to him, C'mon now, baby, give it up, and Marv and Poppy said, Come on now, Charles, give it to her and let's see, and I was thinking, Goddamn, goddamn, and suddenly Charles stood up and threw it down on the table. There, you blond bitch, let's see it. And she gave him a big wink, slipping the money off the table and out to the center of the floor.

Then she was turning her back on the crowd as she began wiggling out of her mink coat, throwing it in the center of the floor. A purple brassiere and purple panties, that's what she had on, with her high-heeled shoes and white skin, as Charles called out, Hey, Queenie, still nothing, as they all laughed, all across the room and began pounding on the tables, shouting, Nothing, nothing.

Queenie was smiling now, sliding over her coat lying there on the floor, holding her hands out to the men as she passed between their tables, and calling to Charles, Be patient, baby, you'll see it all, just be patient. With all of them sitting there with that look of wishing that they had been the ones to have given her the twenty pounds.

Now she came back to us, just the purple bra and pants. Poppy tried to grab her rear and she slapped him gently, Don't handle the merchandise, baby. Looking at me—Hi, baby, why so quiet?—sitting down on Marv's lap now, her purple bra and pants, her white skin, her blond hair against his face as she pursed her lips at him. And they were all stomping on the floor, banging on the tables now, Take it off, take it off. Then she rubbed his thigh, and I saw beads of sweat on his red face. Goddamn, she was all right, Queenie.

Now she wiggled off his lap out to the front, turning her back on us again, and with just a shrug of her shoulders flicked off her bra and threw it on the floor with her mink. And now turning around to us, bare white breasts, good-sized, as they were pounding the tables, All the way, all the way, and it was all going around, she was slithering between the tables, and Marv saying, Well, how do you like Rhodesia, is it like New York, is Queenie as good as the New York girls? And I thinking, she's damn good, and that Rhodesia was a damn good place.

Now she was wearing a robe—where the hell had she gotten it?—a kind of black transparent robe, and she let it hang about her without closing it, so that you could see her bare breasts. And she was sticking out her tongue, and Charles was standing up and screaming at her, Well, well, and she was cooing back, Take it easy, baby, it'll all come, just give me time—what a bitch—and now turning around again, bending her knee, she was taking off her pants, turning around facing us now, but with her robe closed. And coming toward us now, slithering across the floor—the place was bedlam—stopping at our table and saying to Charles, All right baby, take a good look now, as she pulled apart her robe. And there she was, no man all right, all that black hair—and she was a blonde on top. Ha.

They were all applauding now, standing up to see better, and she was taking Charles's hand saying, And what do you think now, baby? But Charles wasn't doing any thinking then, he was just nodding his head with his mouth open, and she put his hand across her white stomach, holding it there, as I drank up, trying to look unconcerned—but I could see everything, and my feet were pounding up and down under the table. Then she slid his hand up her body, across those breasts, saying, Thanks, baby, sticking her tongue just through her lips and sliding his hand down her stomach and onto her thigh, across her black hair, as Charles sat there, not saying a word, his eyes rolling in their sockets.

Then slithering away again, slipping into her mink, they were all standing up and applauding now, Queenie, Queenie, they were calling. Queenie, Queenie, she was damn good, and Rhodesia was a damn good place.

Later she came over to the bar, all dressed, and joined us for a beer. Marv introduced her to me, he seemed to know her very well, her name was Agnes. It was the first time I had ever spoken to a stripper, and she said she'd love to come to the States, she'd never been there, and I told her she'd get a great reception.

Then she said she would have to go—her husband picked her up every night after work—and I marveled how matter-of-factly she said it, as though she sold hats or something.

And they introduced me to more of their friends, and everyone agreed, Yanks were all right, and Rhodesia was really a great place, except that they had this problem about the Kaffir. But really there was nothing to worry about, it wasn't as people abroad tried to make it out to be, surely I could see that. They had him under control, they knew how to take care of him. And he was not good for much anyway.

Then Marv said to me, Look, why didn't I come out to his farm tomorrow when they went back, I could stay a couple of days with him out there. They would all be coming back to Salisbury in a few days. I could come in with them. And without even thinking, I said, Sure I'd love to, and he said, Great, and told Poppy and Charles, Great, we'll show him the real Rhodesia.

People were filtering out now, and Marv said maybe we should call it a night, but Poppy said, No, let's get some steak, it's only three o'clock, they don't close until five.

So we did, and Charles was the first one in the car, and as he stepped in he fell right on his face, unconscious. He had passed out. So we threw him into the back, and we three sat up front. In the restaurant there was a very fat Greek woman behind the counter, who had something wrong with her feet, because they were as big as tree stumps. Poppy called out to her, Hey, gimp, as she smiled embarrassedly and shuffled off for our steak.

She brought us plates of steak with eggs, sausages, potatoes and bread. And I was very hungry but not that hungry, and Poppy kept saying, C'mon, Yank, can't you eat?

Then a couple walked in, the same one that Charles had had the row with. They noticed us sitting at the counter, and sat down at the booth farthest from us. But Poppy saw them, and swaggered over to them, and Marv stood up and followed him, and I thought My God, no, they're really going to get him this time. But no, Marv was pulling Poppy away, C'mon, Poppy, it's late, let's go home.

When suddenly Poppy screamed out, Goddammit, Marv, leave me alone with the bastard. And the girl began to cry, and then

Poppy swinging at Marv, his buddy Marv, the best in the world, Marv ducking, then landing one right into Poppy's gut, and Poppy doubled over. And Marv lifting his knee into Poppy's jaw as he groaned and fell to the floor, delivering the *coup de grâce* in the form of two kicks to the side of his head as he lay there.

The couple disappeared out the door, as Marv went back to his steak, with Poppy groaning occasionally there on the floor. Then Marv took a glass of water and threw it over him. Poppy groaned again and rolled over, and looked up, put his hand to his head and groaned again. Afterward we had to lift him to the car, Marv and I, and we threw him in the back with Charles.

Then it happened as we were driving back to the hotel, just Marv and me, the other two fast asleep in the back—just after Marv had said he'd pick me up at noon tomorrow, just what I didn't want to happen, but what I knew was going to. Mary said, Say, what kind of work do you do? And I said, I'm a teacher, and he nodded, looking straight ahead at the road. And after a while he said, Where, in the States? And I guess I could have said, Yes, and whole thing would have ended, but I said, No, I'm working in Tanganyika, and he said, Oh.

Then after a while he said—still looking straight ahead—Who do you teach? And I said, Tanganyikans. And a little later he said, still looking straight ahead all this time, You mean Kaffirs, and he turned his head, looking at me now for the first time.

And I said, Tanganyikans, Africans, and he gave a short whistle through his teeth, as if to say, I never would have believed it, we took him all over Salisbury and what does he do, he teaches Kaffirs.

And I knew I'd never see him again.

.     .     .

It was twelve o'clock when I woke up, and my head felt as big as a watermelon, and in fact I could feel the pits as I shook it and stumbled into the shower.

Then I was downstairs, checking to see if there were any messages, maybe I had read Marv all wrong last night.

None.

So I walked around downtown . . . the tall buildings, all the cars, and the people, ladies, white ladies, dressed in summer cottons with high heels, and the largest hairdos I have ever seen—bouffants, is that the word?

It was warm and sunny and breezy at the same time, and their skirts fluttered in the wind. And the sidewalks wide and white, and cars and cars rushing and honking, long, sleek American cars, a city in America, not New York perhaps, but maybe Dallas or Miami. Right in the heart of Africa.

I walked up one main street and down another, past the Bank of America, Lloyds of London, Rothman Tobacco. Past supermarkets and drugstores, people walking briskly, white people. And it was the noise, no, more, the pulse, that was it, and I wanted to stand there in the middle of that wide, white pavement and feel the throb of the city bustle past me.

And the Africans. They are there, not many, you see them at the entrance of big buildings, holding the door for the white people. And they say, Good morning, baas, yes, baas. Or you pass them on the street in twos or threes, in poor old clothes. They step aside to let you pass, and talk among themselves in their own language. They look so tired, so sad, so beaten, you don't even dare to speak to them.

And I thought of Ushirika or Tukuyu, where they all seemed so gay, so alive, running and throwing their arms around each other, *Broo, broo,* how are you, *broo?* Or the teachers every morning, slapping hands, Hello, *broo,* how's this morning, how's the teaching?

Then I saw a bus approaching, and suddenly I had this wonderful idea, that I would take it, just to see where it went and who was on it, what they looked like, where they lived. So I walked over to the curb, and as it approached, I looked up at . . . all black faces inside. And I wasn't quite sure whether I could take this bus, maybe it was an Africans-only bus. But I didn't think they had this in Rhodesia. It was the strangest thing, the strangest feeling that came over me standing there on the curb as I let the bus pull away.

So I decided to have lunch instead, and I went into a coffee-shoppish place and ordered some hamburgers—I'm a big man on hamburgers when I'm on the road. And a man who was sitting at the next table, hearing me order I guess, said to me in a very English accent, Aren't you an American?

181

Yes, and he asked me what I was doing here in Rhodesia, and I told him I was trying to go all the way down to the Cape, and he asked me where I had come from, so I told him about Tanganyika. Then he asked me if I meant to tell him that I taught Africans, and I felt like saying, Look, I don't mean to tell you anything, thinking he was going to get up and leave, something like Marv last night.

But no, the man said he was the president of a school board of some kind, he was very interested in this teaching, perhaps I'd consider the possibility of speaking to them about my work in Tanganyika, he knew they'd be very much interested in hearing what I had to say.

Sure, I said, except that I wasn't planning to stay here more than a few days, especially considering the sixty-five shillings I was paying at the Ambassador.

Then as we finished he suggested that if I wasn't doing anything this afternoon, maybe I would like to adjourn to his office, which was quite near, and discuss my experiences at greater length. He'd really like to hear my opinions on certain things.

So I said, O.K., what else did I have to do this afternoon? And he started to pay my bill but I wouldn't let him, and we walked a few blocks, then into one of the biggest buildings, with an African in a uniform and a red cap opening the door for us, Good afternoon, baas, to each of us. Then in the elevator, another African in a uniform who asked us, What floor please, baas, and down a corridor through two swinging doors and another door with a glass sign which said STERN AND COHEN, ATTORNEYS AND REALTORS, and then I knew my problems were over.

He told me that he was Mr. Stern. And he was delighted when I told him who I was. You don't say, he kept saying over and over again, a Jewish boy working in Tanganyika, you don't say, you don't say, as he ushered me into his office with a big red rug, and sat down behind a big desk.

Well, how was it? he wanted to know. How are they? You actually do teach them, do you?

Yes, I said, and in fact they were very bright.

He didn't say anything for a while, just looking down at his hands folded in front of him. Then slowly, almost menacingly, he began to bite off his words, Well, they're not very bright here. All they've got, all they ever had, is what we Europeans gave them.

And he told me to look at this city. We built that, he said, The roads, the farms, we did it. Not they. We. Our labor, he said, our ingenuity, our money. These farms, the Europeans built them with their own hands.

Did I know that when the white man came here, the country was nothing? People living just as you see them now in Tanganyika, no doubt. Did I know that all they had before the white man came was their tribal wars? What kind of life was that? he wanted to know. If they didn't starve, what did they have to look forward to? Only the end of a spear.

And this bloody Nkomo, he said. Did I know that he was no better than the worst of them? Did I know that he had never renounced the use of force, the use of war? Did I know that all he wanted to do was to kick the white man out, to give away everything that we built, give it to the African? Yes, he told me, Nkomo has said as much. He has no concern for the white man. He doesn't even care what happens to the country so long as the white man is driven out. He doesn't care if once the white man goes they revert right back to their old tribal ways.

And did I know what would happen if the white man should go? This country will drift right back to where it was a hundred years ago, back to their raids and killings and massacres. Savages, that's what they are, savages. And without the white man this country would be nothing.

He sat back now as if exhausted. I didn't feel much like listening to this harangue, so I asked him how long he had been out here, hoping that it would get him off on a quieter tack, while not offending him.

But it didn't do any good, because after he said that he had come out here twenty years ago as a young man just qualified to practice law—he had come because of his health—he was proud to say that twenty years later he could boast one of the largest law practices here in Salisbury. And did I know that even in those twenty years there had been such growth, such prosperity, such vast improvement in the country? These buildings, these offices —and he pointed expansively out the window—they had all been built since the war. And it was the strong influx of the European that did it. We're the ones who have created Rhodesia, who have made it what it is today. And the sooner they realize that in Britain and in other places, that it is the European and no one else that has made this country, then the better off everyone, both black and white, will be.

Because they, men like himself, they knew the African, what he was like, how he lived and how he should be treated. What did they know overseas? They would only see a few there, only the brightest of them, because only the brightest went overseas—sometimes he thought they should send some ordinary Africans overseas so they would see what they were really like.

And did I know what the really sad, the pathetic thing was? It was that they listened to those few who went overseas about how they were mistreated over here. Mistreated. Could I believe that? Did I see how much better the African lived here in Rhodesia than in Black Africa? Like in a place such as Tanganyika? Did I know that the standard of living in Rhodesia was the second-highest standard of living for the Africans in all of Africa? And did I know where it was highest? Yes, in South Africa. And look how they talked about South Africa in the United Nations and other Communist places. And he said, You can talk about independence, freedom and the lot, but they are better off right here under us, the white man, where we know how to treat them and where we know how to look after them and care for them.

And did I know that most of them, nearly all of them except for some of their leaders, who didn't care about the ordinary African anyway—all they wanted was power for themselves—did I know that most of them didn't even want independence? Did I know that they wanted it just the way it was? Like his servants, he said, they would plead with him not to leave. They would say, Please baas, don't go. We need you. What will we do if you go? And he would say to them, But your leaders will help you—not believing it for a minute, of course—but just to see what they would say. And they said to him, Baas, our leaders don't care about us, they only want what belongs to the white man.

And he said I shouldn't think it was just him talking, or just his servants. He had a friend, one of the biggest cattle farmers here in Rhodesia, who said the same thing. About how the farm boys would come to him and literally beg him not to leave. Saying just what Mr. Stern's servants had said to him.

Yes, they know, most of them. They know. They remember, the old ones, the chiefs, what it was like before the white man came.

The chiefs voted for the white man to stay, voted for this very government—did I know that? Their chiefs, their leaders, they knew.

Just then a little African tiptoed into the room with two cups of tea, placing them gently on the desk and backing out of the room, so as not to disturb us. And I took this opportunity to delve into my basket of assorted questions for these occasions, as I asked him about the Jewish community here, which I thought would give me a fair chance of getting off on another tack.

He began telling me about the number of families, the number of synagogues, that the community was quite a wealthy one, actually, extremely wealthy now that he thought of it, and I said I recalled reading someplace that the whites of Rhodesia have the highest standard of living in the world.

He raised his eyes at that, but said now that I mentioned it, he wasn't taken completely by surprise. And I asked him if he thought there might be any connection between the high standard of the whites and the low wages paid to African laborers.

But he didn't seem to get the point. Instead he said he wanted to call the rabbi now, to let him know about me and to see if they could not find a place for me to stay for the next few days I would be in Salisbury. Hey, that's really nice of you; thanks a lot, I said.

And he asked me just to wait outside while he phoned and I wondered exactly what he was going to say about me that he didn't want me to hear.

In about five minutes a buzzer rang, which I took to mean that I could come back in. He said he had arranged for me to go to the rabbi's house, he wasn't there himself just now, but his wife was. She said that I should come immediately, and that she would arrange everything for me. He gave me the address and said he was going to call a taxi, and I should first stop by the hotel and collect my luggage.

So I thanked him again, and he said he hoped to see me before I went on, perhaps have another chat. Some chat.

I was very well read, he added. I guess that remark about the living standards of the whites had impressed him.

Then he said what he really wanted was for me to have a true picture of Rhodesia, not just what I had heard from other people who really didn't understand the situation. By meeting the real

Rhodesian, who I could take it from him was an extremely warm and hospitable person—by meeting with him I could begin to get the real picture.

I agreed with him and thanked him again. Somehow the question of my speaking for his school board had been quietly and completely forgotten.

.   .   .

The taxi took me outside the city, where the streets were lined with tall heavy trees, and brick colonial houses were set behind thick bushy hedges surrounded by flowing green lawns. With rows of flowers, purples and reds and oranges, with Africans standing on each lawn in twos and threes, mowing or pruning or seeding, like the boys at Ndumulu.

Then we turned into a crunchy pebbled driveway and as I stepped out of the taxi a woman came out of the house, with two little dogs nibbling at her feet. With a very British accent she said I must be the young American, she was Mrs. Bloom, and I introduced myself. They were just having tea in the drawing room— Won't you join us?—and I couldn't help thinking of Mrs. Stark.

I followed her into a large white house, through a hallway with three Africans in white uniforms parading back and forth from the living room to the kitchen, one carrying a tray of tea things, the second a plate of little sandwiches, and the third some biscuits. Two women were sitting in the living room, one about the same age as Mrs. Bloom, the other younger, late twenties I would say, maybe her daughter. Mrs. Bloom introduced me as This Young American, so I told her my name again, figuring she had forgotten. The others were a Mrs. Mayer and her daughter Jillian, who was working for a copper mine company in Kitwe in Zambia. She was just home for a week on holiday, she said.

Mrs. Bloom poured me some tea as the two servants with the sandwich plate and the biscuits followed her around the room.

Just what was it I was doing here? they wanted to know.

So I told them about Tanganyika, and they all said, Really, with raised eyebrows . . . as though I weren't a Jewish boy after all.

How are you enjoying your holiday? I asked Jillian, and she smiled, All right. But then her mother said, Jillian likes it fine but, oh dear, when *will* she get married? And Jillian blushed and said I'm sorry, Mother, but I just haven't met anyone yet. Then her

186

mother turned to me and asked, Didn't I think it was high time that a girl of Jillian's age and good looks should be married? There are so many young men but she just doesn't seem to be interested, I don't know why—looking at me as though I were the right person to sympathize with her. Then she heaved a huge sigh, and Mrs. Bloom said, Really, Jane.

A short man walked into the room, and Mrs. Bloom called, Hello, dear, and I stood up and he said in a blustering but friendly tone, Is this the young man? So you're the Jewish boy from New York, eh? News seemed to travel fast around here. Just like Ushirika.

Yes, he knew New York well. Been there many times. And did I know Temple Emanu-El? Yes—and he said, See, dear, the boy knows Temple Emanu-El. In New York.

Well, he went on in the same blustering-friendly tone, how did I like Rhodesia? Beautiful country, wasn't it? Quite a change from Tanganyika, he imagined. Maybe you've read about us in the papers, how they say we mistreat the blacks, many people complaining about what we are doing down here. But we know we are right. We know these people.

Then he said to me, What are they like in Tanganyika? and for a moment I didn't know what he meant—what are *who* like? But then I caught on, and I said, Oh, like you and me, I guess, because I didn't know what else to say, and he looked at me and said, Really! . . . But surely you don't mean to say that they feel the same things we do? And I couldn't believe it—was there something we could feel that was so different from what they felt? If you prick us, do we not bleed? . . .

Oh dear, said Mrs. Bloom, suddenly getting up and hurrying in the direction of the kitchen, something's burning. I can smell it. Then shaking her head over to Mrs. Mayer, You know it's always the same when you have a new boy.

A new boy. Did she mean me?

You always have to keep reminding them, they're so forgetful. And Mrs. Mayer saying, And once you've taught them, then they're up and getting cheeky and wanting more money.

And Mrs. Bloom screaming into the kitchen, Harry, Harry. That servant, that's who they had been talking about. Harry. He was sixty if he was a day. Calling him boy. He was almost old enough to be her father.

By the way, the rabbi said to me, who is your rabbi?

In New York?

Yes. Oh—as I told him—yes, I know the man. And calling to the kitchen, Lillian, I know the boy's rabbi.

Mrs. Bloom scurried back into the living room. Oh dear, I told him just ten minutes on each side. But they don't listen. It's so hard to teach them. What was it that you said, dear?

I know the boy's rabbi, Lillian. In New York.

Oh, she said, that's nice, dear. And she shook her head—They just don't listen—as she trotted back to the kitchen.

Maybe I would like a swim, Jillian said. She was just going to take one herself. Hadn't I seen the swimming pool in the back? So I dug my bathing suit out of my bag and they gave me a room to change in, and when I came out Jillian had changed, and the rabbi was saying I shouldn't worry, they were getting me a place to stay that night, I should swim now and then stay for dinner.

Jillian led me outside to the back across a soft fat lawn, and the grass felt good under my bare feet, and there was a tennis court built back against the hedges. Do you play? she asked, as I followed her to the pool, and we lay down on the grass.

There was an African mowing the lawn on the other side, the lulling noise of his motor, the sun brushing on my body. Then splash, Jillian was in the pool, another splash, me too, and the water was cool in the hot sun. And how long it was since I'd been in somebody's swimming pool. Not bad for a rabbi.

Later at dinner, there was a young man who had come, Thruston —his place was where I was going to spend the next three days, the rabbi said, it was the minimum a person had to spend here in Salisbury to really see the city.

And Jillian was saying something again about how she just couldn't believe that I was really working in Tanganyika, with those, those—she was struggling to get the word out—those *mundts,* she finally spat out, which I assumed was a synonym for *Kaffir.* Why couldn't she just call them Africans?

But really, I said, they, the schoolboys at least, are a lot like you and me, and she looked up and wailed, Mother, he keeps saying that.

They're no damn good, Thruston muttered, and Mrs. Bloom told a joke about Africans and then Thruston said, There was one I heard, about an African, a delegate to the United Nations I think it was, who when he checks in at his hotel in New York signs his name X X as he doesn't know how to write. And the man behind the desk says to him, How come you signed with two X's, why not just one X? And do you know what the African answers him? The first X is for Doctor.

It was nearly ten o'clock when we left, Thruston and I. Jillian told me that she would pick me up the next morning and show me around a little if I wanted her to, and the rabbi said that he was leaving on business for Bulawayo, which is about 250 miles south, and would be back in a few days. And Mrs. Mayer said maybe I would come to dinner at her house some night before I left. I think she had an eye on me for Jillian.

Then we were driving with the top down through darkened streets lit by fluorescent lamps, the night blowing softly on us. You could see the shadows of the trees and shrubs, and little lights from the houses set back off the road. And suddenly I had the strangest feeling, driving there in the night, that it wasn't Rhodesia at all, not Africa, but that we were really in America, in the little town in Long Island where I was born.

We turned up a hill and into a driveway that curved in a big circle, and then the outline of a long lawn, and a big house with the lights on. Inside there was a big living room with a thick red carpet and a winding staircase.

There was an old man sitting with a drink in his hand, Thruston's father, and he said to me, I understand you've been working in Tanganyika, and before I could say anything, Well, do you think you understand the African? And before I could say anything again, he said, Well, I do.

He told me that he knew them—how they think, how they work, that they're lazy, that they need a good hiding now and then, that they laugh at each other when they are caught stealing or lazing around and get beaten. Yes, we know how to get them to work. And did I know how that was? It's the way we treat them down here, he said, nodding his head, showing them who is boss, because if they see that the boss isn't tough enough, or not strong, well, they just take advantage and cut up.

And he told me how when he tried out a new bossboy—I inferred that he meant an African because he used the suffix boy—they tried to take advantage of him at first. Well, finally he caught one of them lolling around and brought him in front of the others and beat him until he was nearly dead while they all laughed and howled. And once they had seen that he was strong, that he was willing and able to beat them within an inch of their bloody lives, once they saw this, they never bothered him or acted up again.

Because it is only strength that they respect, he said, only force. And you people who come here with your ideas, trying to change the African and us, trying to change our country and the way we run it, well, you should just remember it's our country, we're Rhodesians, we're behind Smith and independence one hundred per cent. Yes, he said, nodding his head vigorously—and I couldn't help thinking of Mr. Twakatulu—if it comes down to it, we'll fight those hypocritical English bastards, we don't want to be ruled by anyone, or told what to do by anyone. And I could take it from him, he meant every word he said.

Why, just look at the Congo, that's the perfect reason not to give them independence. Those bloody, bloody—he was struggling for the word the way Jillian had—Africans. Must have said Africans to please me. To show me he wasn't prejudiced.

Not that I don't like them, he said. I do. We all do, he said. You have only to look at my Malawi boy in the house. You'll see him tomorrow, he has been with me for forty years. What do you think he would do if I left him? Why he'd starve. He's as good as told me that.

But independence, not on your life. If they try it, we are going to fight, you can tell that to your American friends and that bloody pack of Communists at the United Nations.

And with that he dramatically announced that he was going to bed. People like these, he said—obviously referring to me—made him tired.

.    .    .

I knew it was late when I awoke the next morning. There was the noise of a lawn mower outside, and I pushed open the two doors of my bedroom that opened onto a balcony, and there stretching green and hilly beneath me was the back lawn, acres and acres, like a golf course. And in the middle a blue swimming pool, sparkling like a jewel in the sun.

There were some Africans on the lawn, the one with the mower, and two others sitting on their heels, pulling out weeds and crab-grass, it looked like. And seeing me standing up there on the balcony in only my drawers, they began laughing to each other, pointing to me, as I waved down to them.

When I came downstairs, an African in a white uniform who looked about seventy if he was a day—the Malawi boy, no doubt —asked me, What does the baas want for breakfast? So I told him bacon and eggs, and he scrambled off to the kitchen in that high-stepping run.

Then he was back, handing me a note from Thruston who had gone to work—he worked for his father—he hadn't wakened me because I was sleeping so soundly. He suggested I go to the pool round about eleven, as the sun was specially good there at that hour. He would be back for dinner and then we would go out and meet some of his friends.

So after breakfast I lay out by the pool and let the morning sun bake me all over, and then I was splashing in the cool water, and later lying on the grass, delicious in the heat with the green grass sloping and the purple flowers, with the far-off sound of the Africans laughing to themselves, the drone of the mower.

Then Jillian came—in a convertible—and she moved over to let me drive, the sun warm on our faces and the breeze soft. She turned on the radio as we purred through the suburbs, past the houses with the big lawns and the bushy hedges and beautiful purple flowers. And past a country club where they were all standing in whites on a carpet lawn—they were playing bowls, Jillian said.

Then we drove into Salisbury because Jillian wanted to buy some shoes for someone, and into a Bata shoe store, with only Africans inside. Jillian said that Europeans usually didn't like to buy these shoes—her friend liked them, though—as five African salesmen ran up to her, surrounding her. Could they help her? Thrusting pairs of shoes at her, and calling to me, Baas, baas, look at this one, baas. And I couldn't help thinking of Tanganyika, where people were always running up to you, *Broo, broo,* trying so hard to be friendly, always so enthusiastic, as that is how they thought you wanted them to be, it seemed. And here in the Bata store, that was really all these Africans had done, only trying to wait on her, to please.

But Jillian just flicked them away with a whisk of her hand, a curt, really rude, offhand, superior toss of her head. No, no, no, she shouted at them as they stood there falling all over themselves, each one holding a pair of shoes, trying to catch her attention.

Later she drove me through the townships—the areas in which the Africans lived. Just outside Salisbury, where the tarmac turned to dirt, little brick houses—about the size of mine at Ndumulu—along the side of the road, set on dirt lots, no grass. Some of their doors were open and you could see inside as we drove past, a little gas stove in each house through the opened doors.

Jillian said that the government had built these houses for the Africans. Did I notice how many of them had stoves? How did that compare with Tanganyika? Yes, she said, they took care of the African here in Rhodesia. Did I know that these houses were specially built by the government, only for Africans, and given to them free of charge? Where in Black Africa did the government do this?

But the houses were so small and seemed so crowded—the stove seemed to fill the whole room—and the streets were littered with garbage that hadn't been picked up in weeks, it seemed. And the Africans were sitting around their houses or walking aimlessly about, the children barefoot and in dirty rags. Why didn't she ask me how that compared with Tanganyika?

Then we were driving back to Thruston's house, it was getting on in the afternoon. We drove past the houses and the long sweeping green lawns, and we could see people playing tennis in their own fenced courts or swimming in their pools, and I hadn't noticed before how many of them had their own private courts and pools in their back yards. And somehow it didn't seem to make any difference what it was like in Tanganyika, how the African lived there. How could you compare Tanganyika to Rhodesia, with its big cities like Salisbury, where all the white people lived in their big houses with their green lawns and bushy shrubs, with their swimming pools and tennis courts?

We decided to stop for a bite at a little restaurant just off the road. Inside were some girls, dancing to a jukebox, white girls not more than fifteen or sixteen years old, and others at tables, Cokes and hamburgers, an African running up, bringing us water, another running to take our order, Yes, baas. And cars were pulling up outside, young people, teen-agers—I guessed they came here after school—in tight pants, the girls with those horrible bouffant hair-do's, all wiggling to the music now.

And I thought back to Tanganyika at night, listening to the

music of Radio South Africa and Lourenço Marques, the funny faraway feeling I would have hearing those songs. How it seemed so far away from Tanganyika, so close to home, how this was what we used to do after school when I was a teen-ager, pulling up in our cars to a little place like this, sipping Cokes and munching hamburgers, dancing to the jukebox.

But being here now, seeing it like this, there was somehow something depressing about it all, something about the Africans running around like that taking your order. Yes, baas.

How easy life was here, what a pretty country, what a good life. Tennis courts, swimming pools, country clubs. The rabbi with his synagogue, Mrs. Bloom with her Hadassah meetings no doubt.

But there was something wrong about it all, something that made me uneasy, not so much the way they were living there, but the way they were living compared to the African. Because how could you compare the African in Rhodesia to the African in Tanganyika? What did Rhodesia have to do with Tanganyika? No, it was the black in Rhodesia compared to the white. Because Rhodesia was somehow more like America than it was like Africa or Tanganyika. Those townships were somehow more like Negro slums than they were like African villages.

And what really got me depressed, I guess, was seeing those Africans, in that horrible way they had of running after the white man crying, Baas, baas, yes, baas. Or standing in the entrance of buildings, holding the door, stepping aside as you passed them on the sidewalk. Somehow all this talk about their living better than in Tanganyika didn't matter one damn bit, not when you saw them here like this.

. . .

I left Salisbury the next morning. Thruston had said there was a party Saturday night, I definitely should stay for it, and Jillian had said it was the least I could do after she had shown me around. And the rabbi had even phoned from Bulawayo to ask if there was anything wrong.

No, I said, I just had to get going south. So I was standing on the road, it was a perfect day for hitchhiking, warm and breezy, and the road was tarmac so I didn't have to worry about dust swirling in my face with each passing car. Maybe I could make the border tonight with luck.

G

Soon a car stopped for me and we were off, the road was straight and the land was flat, the sky racing down on top of us through the front windshield, with thick green forests on both sides. Past little towns with only a few wooden stores along the main street, with white people scurrying briskly about and groups of Africans lolling aimlessly on the sidewalk, then—*whoosh*—you were out into the country again.

And strangely enough, maybe because of the flatness, it reminded me of Suffolk County in Long Island, out toward Montauk in the summer, the potato fields stretching row after row, the same whooshing in and out of little towns with strange Indian names, Quogue, Patchogue, Ronkonkoma . . .

And here now the land was just as flat, the towns just as small—*whoosh* and you're out—the names of the towns just as foreign, Que Que, Gwelo, Shangani. Except that there were so many Africans, half naked, barefoot, that endless stream of traffic along the road, with bundles and baskets on their heads—where were they all coming from and where were they all going? And their mud huts, cone-shaped roofs, bunched together in groups of thirty or forty on the sides of the road. And I was suddenly conscious of the fact that there were many of them, very many. What is it the books say—they outnumber the whites twenty to one?

Later a young man and his girl friend, sitting huddled together in the front seat, picked me up. He was talking to her in very low tones, squeezing her to him, and I couldn't catch most of what he said. Then as we passed an African woman who was selling baskets by the side of the road, he said to his girl, How'd you like one of those baskets, honey? No, John, she said, I don't want one, and he said, Sure you do. He winked back to me, I'll just stop and get the little lady a gift without even paying for it, and to her, Watch, I won't have to pay anything for it, honey, and he slowed down the car as if to stop.

And I pictured him getting out of the car, going over to the African woman with her baskets, taking one, and her not saying anything, just sitting there expecting him to give her the money. And him walking back to the car, the lady thinking, Maybe he is going back to the car to get the money. And then his getting in and just driving off, the poor woman still sitting there—what could she do now?

But the girl said, No, really, John, really, I don't want one, and finally he said, O.K., and speeded up again. And I wondered what I would have done if he really had stopped the car.

He let me off near a diner, and I went in and grabbed a hamburger. It was late in the afternoon now, becoming dark, and I still had a long way to go before the border, and it was getting colder too, so I took a sweater from my bag, wondering where I was going to spend the night if I didn't get another ride.

But then it came, a big new Oldsmobile; the driver was going to Beitbridge tonight—the border—Johannesburg tomorrow. Let's go.

Very quiet, in his fifties I would guess, he said he ran a fishing camp near Wankie, wherever that was—that he was going to Johannesburg to visit his little boy for Christmas. But he didn't say anything else so we left it at that, and I watched the country pass, much dryer now, with fewer trees, spaced more widely apart, and more clusters of those cone-shaped African mud huts.

Now in the dimming light, you could occasionally catch the outline of a deer crossing the road ahead. And once we came close to hitting one—why didn't he slow down? Then there was an old African walking along the side of the road leading two old cows, when suddenly one of them bolted into the middle of the road . . . the screeching of brakes, the car turning halfway around as the cow loped off to a field now, the old man chasing after it with his stick.

The driver was out of the car, screaming something at the old African in some native dialect. The African stopped in his tracks and walked meekly back to the car, his head bowed. The driver grabbed the stick out of his hand, shaking it at him while the African looked down at the ground, not making a sound or a motion. How many times had this happened to him before, I wondered? Finally the driver gave him a kick in his rear, snapping the stick across his knee as the African trudged off.

Then we were at the border, Beitbridge, filling out forms. Over the bridge, the Limpopo River beneath us in the darkness, in a few miles Messina. We would stop for gas there, he said, and maybe get a drink.

So we stopped at the first gas station and got out. It was very hot outside—wondered why I hadn't noticed it before—with long fluorescent light bulbs over the pumps, and along the lights thousands of giant flying ants, swarming, filling the night with their wings, without any sound. I couldn't help thinking of the Swahili word for flying ants which the boys had taught me, *kumbi-kumbi*.

An African in a red uniform scurried over to us—Yes, baas, and began filling the tank. A group of African girls was standing around and watching us, pretty girls, young, their hair cut short like the Tanganyikans', but wearing very short skirts that didn't quite come down to the knees, and red berets that sat jauntily on their heads. They seemed to be smiling coyly at us, or was it a leer? Because it is against the law in South Africa for a white to go to bed with a black.

Then we drove across the street to a bar, where some men were laughing together and playing darts, and I bought the first round and then the driver bought me one, as more people kept coming in.

The bartender saw that we were strangers and began talking to us, as I bought another round. Then the bartender stood us a round. Call me Duke, he said, so we introduced ourselves to him and to each other for the first time, the driver's name was Jack Something-or-other.

He began talking about his fishing camp in Wankie, how Stanley Holliday, the Minister of something had once stayed there for three days. And he fished out a letter from his wallet that Stanley Holliday had written him about what a nice time he had had.

Then they asked about me and I told them all about how I was coming from Tanganyika and wanted to go all the way to Capetown.

But what do you do? Jack asked, and I said, I'm a teacher.

Wait a minute, he said. Are you telling me you teach those bloody *mundt* kids? I nodded my head, and he said, Well, I'll be damned, and whistled through his teeth the way Marv had 'that night in Salisbury. Then he looked at Duke standing behind the bar and he banged his fist down, You know I took this bastard nearly a hundred and fifty miles, and I was going to take him with me to Johannesburg tomorrow.

And I couldn't believe I was hearing correctly. I started to say, Just wait a minute, Jack, but he was going on, speaking to Duke, but really to me, that I could get my bag out of his car right now.

And I could feel it coming up inside of me, saying to him, You just give me the keys, you stupid bastard, what the hell do I need you for to take me to Johannesburg? And him cocking his arm, as if he were going to swing, and quick Duke grabbing him—how had he gotten around from behind the bar?—and saying, Now take it easy, Jack, this boy only wants to see the country. What's he going to think if you are acting this way, how is he going to learn what it is really like down here?

Yeah, but he teaches Kaffirs, Jack said.

But if he wants to come here and see the country, see South Africa, what's wrong with that? Jack didn't say anything now, he was just staring past Duke's shoulder across the bar.

Yes, he should see Pretoria, the capital, Capetown, Johannesburg, travel the Garden Route, visit Durban, the Transkei . . . Jack said nothing, just looking sullenly out in front of him.

Just give me the keys, I said to Jack. I was taking my bag out of his car right now, whether he liked it or not. And asking Duke if there was any food here. No, but he would personally take me out to a restaurant.

Then we were in Duke's car, driving very fast, to some Italian place, the food heavy and filling—just what I needed—then driving back to the hotel, carrying my bag upstairs . . . *plop* into bed asleep.

I was on the road by ten the next morning. Duke was the owner of the hotel, I had learned, and he had refused any money for the night. Must have felt guilty about Jack. He had said he wanted me to get the right impression of South Africa, so he had written down a whole list of places for me to see and friends of his who would put me up. Just mention Duke and don't worry about a thing, he said.

Soon a husky Afrikaaner stopped for me in a pickup truck. I could tell he was an Afrikaaner because he wore a pointed Robin Hood kind of hat with a little feather tucked in the band, and he spoke to me in Afrikaans—which sounded something like German. There was an African sitting in the front with him, who got out now without a word and went and sat in the back of the truck.

He was going to Potgietersrus, he said, which is about two-hundred miles south of Messina, he wanted to get some part for his tractor. I sat back and watched the country roll out, long and green, beginning to become hilly now. Through sparkling little towns with Afrikaaner names like Louis Trichardt, Banderlierkop, Pietersburg, with blond little children walking along the street in short pants, without shoes, or riding bicycles in their bare feet. Then out again, climbing more, whisking in and out of tunnels cut into the mountains, across bridges where you could look down gorges on either side.

And it reminded me of the Catskills in upstate New York, somewhere north of Bear Mountain, along the Hudson, the same flowing green hills, the same clean little towns with Dutch names, Rensselaerville, Voorheesville, Schoharie. Except that along the roads, outside the towns, you'd see Africans, men, women, with their loads on their heads, or an old wooden cart pulled by a horse, with five or six Africans squeezed into the wagon. And the cone-shaped huts that dotted the countryside, the smoke seeping through the roofs. No, you couldn't forget, as much as you wanted to, you couldn't forget the Africans and the way they lived.

Suddenly the truck screeched to a stop and the Afrikaaner jumped outside and began to yell at an African who was just walking along minding his own business. Then the driver hopped back in the cab, as the African jumped up in the back with the other African, and the farmer said to me, I'm sorry for the delay, I just wanted to give the fellow a lift. I like to help them whenever I can.

We stopped for lunch at a little restaurant and he wouldn't let me pay, and then he had to make a few stops visiting some friends of his along the way. So it was already dark when we got to Potgietersrus, and he said he had only one more stop to make, just to pick up his tractor part, and then he would return. He was sorry he wasn't going farther. Otherwise he would be glad to take me.

So I thanked him and jumped out and headed for the first hotel. There was a man at the desk with a long black handlebar mustache, and, hearing my accent, he asked me where I came from. So I told him about today, and about Tanganyika, and he whistled through his teeth, Must be tough up there. Just like those savages in the Congo, I bet. Here, let me get you some supper, you haven't had any, have you?

He motioned me into his office, and there were two ladies and he introduced us. One was his wife, the other a Mrs. Speck. His name was Jamie. He called an African over. Did I want beer or Scotch? Beer.

And to the African, Bring this *baas* a beer and a lot of meat and some salad; and the African ran off.

He began telling the two women how I had come all the way

from Tanganyika. Mrs. Speck curled her lip and hissed, Those savages, and Jamie's wife said, The poor thing—meaning me. What exactly did I do there? they asked, as though they couldn't believe I was here in one piece. And Mrs. Speck wanted to know whether they were the same as we were, you know, not looks but "mentally wise."

They were, I said, so far as I could see anyway, but she said, No, she would never believe it, it just wasn't true.

The African trotted in with the food, beef, chicken and gobs of salad, and the beer was cold, and it was really nice of Jamie to do this—and I began wolfing it down.

What did I eat up there? they wanted to know. What kind of food, where did I get it? And I told them about bringing the water from the river and having to boil it, buying the meat and vegetables at the market, and that it really was very good food. And I had the feeling that they thought I must be mad, as they sat there wide-eyed, listening to these things I was saying in so matter-of-fact a tone, things I had become perfectly used to. Had I changed so much since I had first arrived in Tanganyika, to live the way I had and not think anything of it? Or was it merely the way the whites in South Africa thought of the African, that a white man must be mad to live among them?

Probably a little of both.

Next morning at breakfast Jamie brought over a young man, Another American, he said to each of us. His name was Tony. He had been working in South Africa six months now, after a year in Liberia. Great place, South Africa, he said.

He was selling tractors. He lived in Johannesburg and traveled during the week. Great way to see the country, he said. Say, maybe I would like to come around with him today, see some of the back country, meet some farmers. He could take me with him to Johannesburg tomorrow. Besides it was his first trip in this area, and he'd need someone to help him with signs and road maps.

Yes, Jamie said, you should go with him. It will be good for you to see South Africa. You'll be my guest here tonight. Just don't worry about a thing.

That seemed to settle it, so after breakfast Tony and I drove out of town a few miles and then turned west into the hills, where the

road became dirt with fields of farmland, sleek and green and rolling, with fat cows grazing—funny how I noticed a good fat cow now
. . . after a year of those scrawny things in Tanganyika.

Then we turned off the main road down another dirt road that
cut across the farmland. It seemed to run for miles, as we whisked
by cattle that were grazing right up to the road, then into a circular
driveway with thick trees, and up to a large ranch-style house set in
the shade. Like a suburban home.

A huge-bosomed woman appeared at the door. She had the same
shape as Mrs. Twakatulu except that she was white. Tony spoke to
her in Afrikaans—I wondered where he had learned it.

The farmer was in the fields, he translated for me. This was his
wife. Why didn't we just sit down under the trees? He would be
along in a minute, she would send a boy to call him.

Soon he came, tall, heavyset, ruddy face, wearing overalls and
that Robin Hood hat. He sat down with us and called something to
his wife, and in a little while she brought out some tea and sandwiches.

Tony explained who he was, that he had come to check on his
tractor, and introduced me to him.

Ah, another American, he sighed. How he would love to go to
America. South African farming was wonderful, but American
farming was even better. What a place that America must be. Then
they started talking tractors a bit, his was fine, working very well,
he was even thinking of ordering another one, as he was opening up
a new stretch of land, and he pointed out behind the trees.

Maybe we would like to stay for lunch, the farmer asked us suddenly, it would be ready soon.

Thanks very much, Tony said. So they talked tractors some
more over soup and salad and stew and cold roast and sausages. I
had never seen this much food at one time for one meal.

Then we were off again, to visit another farmer. Tony said he
lived way up about sixty miles into the mountains, but that he had
two tractors. And the road winding as we climbed into the mountains, the fields stretching for miles and miles, all clean and sleek
and freshly plowed. They were waiting for the rains, Tony said.
And I thought of Tanganyika—they were also waiting for the rains
but there they burned the land instead of plowing it.

It was late afternoon before we reached the place, as we couldn't
go very fast on that road, and we had also made a wrong turn. The

farmer was sitting under his big trees near his large house—in his fifties, I'd say, big and husky—and there were two young men sitting next to him, also big, almost as big as the old man, both in blue overalls, sweaty, as though they had just come in from the day's plowing.

Tony introduced us. The older man was the father, these were his two sons. They lived just down the road, each in his own house with his wife. Two more Mrs. Twakatulus, no doubt.

They seemed very interested when Tony told them about my work in Tanganyika—they looked at each other with raised eyebrows, or was it a sly grin?

What did I think of the African? the old man wanted to know. Did I understand them? Did I realize that the only thing they respected was the stick?

You know, he said, people say I work my boys too hard. Well, maybe I do. But I can tell you one thing, they like me, those boys, they really do. I hear it from farmers who hear it from their own boys. They say they like me because I treat them hard and fair. And I'll tell you what I do, when a boy steals or cheats or gets lazy, or cuts up, or gets drunk, I call them all together and then I beat hell out of him, right there in front of all the others, who stand and roar with laughter. And you know, I never have any trouble from that boy again, he even works harder than he ever did before.

And I couldn't help thinking of Mbaliki, how he had done just that, becoming lazy, cutting up, getting drunk. And that the only way to handle him seemed to be to clamp down on him, a psychological, a more sophisticated stick. Or with Bwana Mchanga . . . how they had all stood around fascinated, afraid to come too close, hanging on my every word—me, the boss. And I remembered how I felt then, as I walked through that crowd opening to let me pass, how easy it was to begin to feel, to begin to think that you were the boss, the chief.

The farmer was going on, I know that America doesn't think that what we do here is right, that they think we are cruel, that we mistreat the African, that we aren't giving him his rights and that kind of thing. Well, I want to tell you something—and his voice was calm and level, no antagonism, no bitterness—they come to me, Baas, we've had an awful fight, one of us has been hurt bad, or Baas, my baby's sick, or it's my wife, Baas, she's dying. And we—myself, my sons—we settle their arguments for them, we drive them to the hospital, we take care of them in our own homes when they're sick or dying.

And let me tell you something else. All these families—and he pointed with his hand in a sweeping semicircle—we have lived on this land for more than two hundred years. We came here with nothing, we found this land bare, probably the way it is in Tanganyika, and now look what we have done . . .

It was bush when we first came here and we cultivated it, plowed it, so that it is as you see it today. We have raised our families here, my sons are raising theirs now. We did it ourselves, all of it, with no help from anyone—no loans, no foreign aid, nothing. And let me tell you, we are not giving up our land, none of it, not to anyone. If it comes to that, we will stand here and fight, the way we fought the British before for our land, me, my wife, my sons, and their sons.

And I thought of them standing there, their big shoulders, their ruddy faces; their huge-bosomed wives; even their little blond children—each with a rifle in his hand. I couldn't help feeling sorry for the poor Africans whom they would be fighting, whoever they might be.

Jamie and his wife and Mrs. Speck were sitting on the terrace at the hotel with drinks, as we drove up that evening. Jamie had taken the afternoon off, he said, they were having a tennis match at the club, and he hadn't wanted to miss it, and he ordered us some drinks. And Mrs. Speck was off again about my work, How can you even think for a minute that they are the same as you and me?

It was all a waste anyway, as far as he could see, Tony said, because if you educated them a little, say through grade eight, then they would just want to go on to secondary school. But there weren't enough schools for them. Yet because they had received just a little education, now they didn't want to go back to the farms any more.

Yes, I mused, that's how it was in Tanganyika. Only in Tanganyika there was nothing for any of them to do if they didn't go back to the farm, because there were just no jobs, and the education they had received didn't equip them for anything practical. What good is history or geography if you don't go beyond Standard 8?

The African brought the drinks and I sipped on mine. The wind

202

nudged me softly, and I watched the lights flickering across the street. Suddenly I didn't want to talk about Tanganyika or think about its problems, it was too nice sitting there on the terrace.

Jamie was talking about the club again, or about a golf tournament that they planned to have next weekend. A car crawled lazily down the street. It was a good life.

•   •   •

Johannesburg. That's where we were going. We had left early that morning so that Tony would have a chance to show me the city, except that his car had broken down, and it had taken until the afternoon to fix it. Then just outside Johannesburg we stopped at a bar for a beer and got to talking with some people who were very interested in Tanganyika, and ended up by eating supper there with them. So by the time we finally got to Tony's apartment, which was all the way on the other side of Joburg, it was nearly midnight. All I could do was flop down on his studio couch—out for the night.

Next morning I received a phone call. It was a youngish voice, a reporter, it said, from the *Rand Daily Mail*. He had heard I was from Tanganyika—someone who had met me last night had phoned to tell him—and they would be interested in doing a story on me. Would I mind?

No, I didn't mind, but I certainly didn't have much I could tell him. Must be hard up for news, if they wanted to do a story on me.

But just the fact that I was here from Tanganyika, that was news. Could he come up this morning?

Tony wasn't very pleased when I told him I was going to be interviewed. The government didn't like this newspaper. They could get you in plenty of trouble, this *Rand Daily Mail*, as they were very antigovernment. Actually the only way I could get myself into trouble was to say something very undiplomatic about Tanganyika, which would be picked up by somebody and eventually trickle back to the Tanganyikans. But I'd be careful.

Tony left before the man from the newspaper came. He was young, maybe about my age, with a round Irish face and a Continental suit that was about three sizes too small for him. Hi, he said very enthusiastically, I'm Jake White, and I want to know all about Tanganyika, everything there is. And he really did want to know, it seemed, not merely for the story, but just to know. And when I said something that surprised him, he would say, Is that so, or You don't say.

But after a while he began to see that I was being quite guarded with my answers. Like he would say, Did I think the Africans were capable of self-government? and I would say, As I was a teacher I didn't have too much to do with the running of the government, so it would be difficult for me to give a fair appraisal. Or, Did I find I was accomplishing anything? and I would say, Well, I came to Tanganyika to teach, and I certainly am teaching.

Finally he asked me how I liked South Africa. Fine, I said, all the people I had met were very friendly, but I hadn't met any Africans, and they were the ones I really wanted to see.

Is that so? he said. And he began telling me about some work he had·been doing with some Indians and African political organizations. How he had been arrested under the 90-Day Detention Act, and kept in solitary for forty-five days. He still saw some members of the group, he said, but the organization wasn't functioning any more. The government had seen to that. Because they kept all the suspected members locked up. And when the ninety days were up, they just rearrested them.

In fact, that's where he was going now—to cover the trial of three saboteurs. Maybe I would like to come along.

So quickly I got out my suit and put on my tie, and we drove in his car—the paper paid for it, he said—and walked into the press section of the courtroom, where there were many other reporters all hunched up and scribbling on their pads of paper.

Jake pointed to the docket where there were three men, an African, an Indian, and a European, all charged with belonging to a group that advocated replacing the present government by a true multiracial society, Jake explained. They could all get the death sentence, but he doubted that they would.

The judge and the barristers were up in front wearing wigs—I had never seen that before except in the movies—and there was a visitors' section, two sections really, one for whites, and the other for non-whites, filled with Africans and Asians, and all sorts of mixed shades in between.

Then the African stood up, a very large man with a massive head, and began reading from a sheet of paper in front of him, as Jake explained that each prisoner was going to deliver his final speech before the judge passed sentence.

He was speaking now, the African, he had acted this way because all doors had been closed to him, there had been no way to express himself. He had not acted out of violence or hatred of the white man, no, it wasn't that, but rather because it was just impossible for a thinking person, an educated man, to exist under these present circumstances, where he had been denied all traces of freedom. He spoke well, almost eloquently, addressing the judge, but really speaking right past him, out to the visitors in the courtroom, the press, the people outside the courtroom who would read the papers tomorrow.

Then the Indian spoke—about how all the universities that had once been open to non-whites were now closed to them, about the jobs and the houses that had once been available to them but were no longer to be had. About the restaurants, the hotels, all of which refused to serve people because of the color of their skin. About their being forced now to move into special Indian districts. About there being no legal way to appeal this, the laws didn't cover them, there was no provision for appealing anything that the government wanted to do to them. What was a man supposed to do?

Then the European spoke, saying about the same thing, that he had acted not for any personal gain—what did he himself stand to gain?—but rather from political, from moral convictions. Could any man stand by?

The lawyer for the defense was speaking to the judge now, a final summation. Not that they hadn't broken the law but that the court should try to understand the reasons why they had acted this way.

And as he spoke I couldn't help feeling that there was something sad, something almost pathetic about this whole trial, the whole appearance of a trial. They had broken the law, these men, they had stood against the government. But it was the law that was wrong, not they. And now they had to defend themselves under the rules of that wrong law.

That night Jake takes me to meet some Indian friends of his. One of them is the brother of the Indian who was on trial this morning, he tells me. We drive through Johannesburg, leaving the downtown, the streets becoming narrower, the buildings more shabby, the faces along the sidewalk darker. Garbage cans overflowing at every corner now, dark little children shrilling in high-pitched voices, scampering between parked cars, the tenements so close together they seem to lean on each other.

We park the car next to an old movie theater, the name written in Indian, and I follow Jake into the streets of the garbage cans and tired buildings, past dirty houses with front plots, no grass, just dirt. Some people pass us and stare—white faces in a non-white neighborhood.

Two thin figures are standing there on the sidewalk. I see them more clearly now as we approach and Jake introduces me to them. Both young, in their twenties, I'd say, although you can never tell with Indians—one with glasses, studious-looking, Flakes his name is, funny name for an Indian, wonder what his real name is. He is a doctor, Jake says. The other one is Nick Cabucci or something. Sounds Italian, even looks Italian. Thin and nervous. They seem to know Jake very well, a little afraid of me.

Come on, they say, there is a shabeen just across the street. It's Flakes's cousin's house, we can drink there.

So we cross the street and walk up the steps of a house into a dimly lit room. It seems like a living room, with some chairs and tables, and a single light bulb hanging from the ceiling, which lights up only the front half of the room. And there in the corner where the light does not reach are two beds placed together, with three people asleep on them, three old women . . . their long gray hair falling across their bodies, that dot in the middle of their foreheads, and their long, flowing saris wrapped around them. Three of them . . . the middle one lying so that her feet are between the heads of the other two and her head is between their feet.

We pass into another room, unlit, only a dim glow from the bulb in the living room. There are two more beds together, three more old women asleep, wrapped in their saris, the same, head to toe. Suddenly one of them sits up and stares at us as we are passing, her mouth falling open, a shudder shaking her shoulders as she falls back to sleep.

And somehow seeing those women gives me the most horrible, frightening feeling. Funny . . . I have seen Africans in their homes sleeping on the floor, and thought nothing of it. I have just come from Fedson's mud hut. Why now does it suddenly disturb me so?

Is it that they're so old? But the Africans were old. Is it that they're so poor? But who can be poorer than Fedson's family? No —I think it must be because Flakes and Nick seem so much like me . . . those old ladies, Flakes's relatives, could just as easily be mine.

Then we are in the kitchen, a gas stove, some tables and chairs. We sit down as they bring us a bottle and put it on the table, no label, it must be home-brewed. A fat African woman gives us each a little glass and places a bottle of water on the table, as Jake pours for all of us.

He tells me that Flakes was educated at the University of Johannesburg when it was still integrated. And that Nick had finished his second year when they closed the university to Asians. Then he went to England. Not so good there, eh Nick? he says, and laughs.

Nick laughs too. It was tough, he tells me. I worked nights as an elevator man. Then as a dishwasher. Those were the only jobs I could get. So I came back. I make more money here now as a bookkeeper.

But what about going someplace else? I say. Isn't there any other place you could go?

Where? he says. Australia, only whites. America, Canada, they have their quotas. India? In India they are starving.

And besides it's harder than you imagine to leave here, where you've grown up, where your father and his father and his father have lived. Remember we Indians have lived in South Africa for generations, many of us for more than a hundred years. They call us Indians, but really we are not. We don't belong in India. Our home is here, in South Africa.

We used to all work together in the Indian National Congress, Jake tells me now. Before. And they all laugh. Before all the leaders were arrested and the party was disbanded.

But we still get together sometimes, Nick says. Yes, did you see that sign near where you are staying? Jake says to me, meaning at Tony's place. There's a big wall with "Apartheid Must Go" scribbled in chalk. That was us, last month.

Now another Indian walks in, very dark, surly-looking. He shakes hands with Nick and Flakes, and the fat African brings him a bottle and glass, and he drinks in silence. Then two colored men—colored means half-white, half-black—in old clothes enter and sit by themselves. And each time as the door opens, Jake tenses as if he is afraid of seeing someone. It's that whites aren't allowed in here, he says. If the police come in here we are in real trouble.

Then a man and a girl come in. The man is swarthy and the girl dark also, but they are whites, I think. They walk past without looking at us and sit down with the two colored men. Later I happen to look up just as they are looking up and our eyes meet. For a split second their glances seem to freeze on Jake and me. I look hard at them now, the man's hair is kinky and curly. No, maybe he is not white. He must be colored. And the girl too, that's why she is so dark. What is it in their eyes as they see Jake and me? What are they feeling that makes their glances freeze on us? Fear, perhaps. No, it isn't fear. Almost embarrassment. That we are white and they are not.

Soon our bottle is empty and everybody seems to be talking to one another, and I notice two other Indians, very broad, standing over the first Indian. He finishes his drink and they walk out together. Somehow they look like gangsters, out of Al Capone days. That's just what they are, Flakes says. They run a distilling plant here in Joburg. They are involved in a war with a colored gang now. When they catch a victim, they do something to his spine to paralyze him. Nice bunch of boys.

Now Flakes is talking about his brother, who was in the trial today. He is to be sentenced tomorrow, he says. The others in the room are all looking at him, their conversation has stopped. And look at me here tonight, Flakes goes on. Drunk, I'm drunk. Getting drunk the day before my brother gets sentenced. Twenty years, that is what they expect him to get. Twenty years. And here I am getting drunk the night before he is to be sentenced. He leans back in his chair. This fucking country, and begins to laugh. Look what it does to you. Look what it is doing to me. Getting drunk before my brother gets twenty years.

Suddenly his voice stops. I turn around in my seat and look in the direction Flakes's head is turned. There in the doorway are two huge men. White men. Not a sound in the room now. We just sit.

The white men say something in Afrikaans to the colored couple. Their voices crackle in the silence. Then they laugh and walk out the door.

Quick, Jake says, let's go. They may come back. So we get up and Flakes says we can go to his house, we can drink some more there.

So we sway off down the street, across a vacant lot, into an apartment building that smells of garbage and urine, with insects crawling out of the walls. There is no elevator so we have to walk up three flights of dark rickety stairs, and then outside up a fire escape.

A dark woman opens the door into a small room. Flakes's wife. And we sit around a small table but we don't drink anymore, we just talk. Flakes's wife is really very nice, but the house is so small, just this little room and a bedroom. And Flakes a doctor. Is this all he can afford? And I wonder if there are any old women sleeping head to toe in the other room.

Later we decide to go for sandwiches in Jake's car. Only Flakes and Nick have to sit in the back so that when someone comes for our order they won't be recognized as Indians. How they must feel every time that happens to them hiding so they won't be recognized for what they are.

And me, what would I do if the person serving us saw them and refused? Would I storm out of the car, shake him by his neck, grab his collar and punch him in the mouth? And I can begin to understand now what they were talking about in the trial when they said that they joined this organization because they had no way of expressing themselves. What do you do when you're not treated as a person? And where the law says it's wrong to treat you as a person?

But they don't spot Nick and Flakes; we eat and then drive off. And soon we have to stop and urinate, so we pile out and Flakes and Nick walk to the biggest, newest car parked on the street, the car that looks as though it belongs to the richest, fattest white man. And they unzip their flies and urinate on that car . . . on the fender, on the door, all over the tire. And it is so sad watching them there, taking out their frustrations and anger on this car, their urine which would be dried up and unnoticed by anyone in the morning.

Oh, apartheid, apartheid, that wretched word. That's what has done it to them. It robs the dignity of every man, tears out his insides and leaves a bitter, twisted shell of a man. Urinating on a white man's car in the dark of the night.


Jake called me the next morning. He was going to visit a friend of his in jail, a girl who had been arrested with him. But she had belonged to the Communist party, and had been tried and convicted and sentenced to five years.

Five years. A Communist. A real Communist. I'd never met one before. What were they like, I had always wondered. Probably some dogmatic intellectual with glasses and long uncombed, unwashed hair. It would be an experience meeting one.

The prison was a converted old fort. We pounded on the knocker and an old woman stuck her face up to the hole in the door and opened it just a crack. Then two hefty matrons ordered us inside, as Jake said the girl's name. One of the matrons plodded off to get her, while the other, with her fat neck and beady eyes, stood and watched us. And all around us bars and the clanging of chains, the squeaking of metal doors, as I waited for the Communist Monster.

But an angel came out instead. A lovely young girl with blond hair and blue eyes and milk-white skin. She looked like the girl you'd want to take to the prom.

Hi, Jake. She smiled. How nice to see you. How have you been? As though we had just dropped by her sorority house.

O.K., Maggie, how are you? How are you getting on?

Oh, she said, it's not too bad. They let me take a bath every other day, and I have a lot of books. It's just the nights that are long. It gets dark at seven, you know, and they don't have any lights. But they said I might be able to get out in two or three years if my behavior is good.

Two or three years. She said it as if it were two or three days. And she was so young, so pretty. Those blue eyes . . . she had a funny, faraway look when she talked to you.

And she had the nicest smile, you just wanted to say to her, Look, what are you doing here? It must all be some mistake. You're so young, you didn't know what you were doing, you couldn't have. You just tell them you're sorry and everything will be all right. They'll know you didn't mean it.

She was talking to Jake now, What are you doing for New Year's? Do you think they'll have a party this year like last year? Speaking in so calm, so matter-of-fact a voice that it was almost scary. And her eyes, she was in another world.

And I suddenly had this funny feeling that if somehow they really were to say to her, Look, just say you're sorry, that you didn't mean it, whatever you did, just apologize and we will let you out—well, I'm not sure she would have done it. Something about her eyes.

Then the matron came and said that our time was up. We stood up to leave, Goodbye, she said to me. Nice meeting you. Goodbye, Jake. I hope I'll see you again soon. As though he had just dropped her off after a date.

．　　　．　　　．

Then I was off again, on the road, this time for Capetown. The first car that stopped was going to Grahamstown, which was near the coast. I could go southeast from there to Port Elizabeth, and then along the Garden Route to the Cape. It was a long ride though, and we had to spend one night on the road in a hotel. Up early the next morning, taking an old dirt road over the mountains, toward the east now instead of south.

Grahamstown, the sea breeze, the road curving along the shore, glimpses of the ocean in the distance. On to Port Elizabeth, grimy and dirty with red-brick buildings and smoke pouring from the chimneys. It reminded me of Manchester, New Hampshire, along the turnpike, factories red and ugly with smoke pouring out of them, with rows and rows of old, gray windows staring out at you as you drive past.

Outside of Port Elizabeth the road turned to the west and soon a young fellow in a Volkswagen picked me up. It interested him that I was an American, especially that I was from Tanganyika. He was going only about sixty miles, he said, he had a summer home where three of his school friends and their friends and their families had been coming year after year. Say, why didn't I come along, they would really be interested in meeting me. Besides it was right near the ocean. I could swim and surf. And they had plenty of beer. Unless I was in a hurry to get to Capetown.

So I did—I wasn't in any hurry. The boys, his friends, were sitting inside, each with a can of beer, boys about my age, with supper already cooked and waiting for us. A Yank, eh, well, give him a can of beer.

They were all students. Bob, the driver, was at Rhodes University in Grahamstown, the others, Biff and Bert, were studying medicine at Capetown. They brought in more beer and they told me that everyone here in South Africa thought that America was the greatest country on earth. There were many American factories here, their troops had fought together with our troops, there was just such a great friendship between the two countries.

But they couldn't understand America's attitude toward them in the U.N., and places like that, the way Americans were always criticizing their government and their way of life. Why was it?

Then they wanted to know about Tanganyika, what was it like for me, what did I do, how did I live, what did I do at night, how were the women? And listening to them, I almost felt as though I were back home in America with my friends, this was just what they would have asked me.

Then Bob asked me about the African. In fact he used the word African. But he said it in such a sneering way that I knew what was coming next. He's not the same as we are, is he? Surely you have learned that now, after a year with them. They just don't think the same, do they? I mean, they're not completely stupid, there are certain things they can do, up to a point. But then they seem to reach a certain level and they can't seem to catch on, no matter how much you train them. They're just not as smart as we are, no two ways about it.

Yes, Biff said, they can never be the same as the whites. Look how none of them go in for math or science. It's only law that the smartest of them go in for. No engineers, no doctors—they can't do math—only politicians, rabble-rousers. Why is it? he sneered at me. They just can't—can't—conceptualize. Yes, that's the word, conceptualize.

Couldn't do math, couldn't conceptualize. How could I begin to explain? How could I get them to see why my boys couldn't understand that picture of the sailor on the boat, or why they thought I was using magic when the ice cubes melted or water boiled?

And could I tell them how easy it was to think that the African was inferior because of this, to just cross him off and say, Well, he can only reach a certain level, or he just doesn't have the intelligence of the whites? Could I begin to explain about Fedson's village, how there was nothing but the fields? That the boys had come to school knowing nothing, a complete blank slate, because there was nothing in that village for them to know, for them to learn? How old had Fedson been when he had first seen a book? All the things we take for granted, we whose parents tell us stories and read us books . . . we who see pictures and advertisements on billboards, who don't even realize that we are learning, that we are being exposed to impressions day after day from the time we are two and three years old. . . .

And then when they do go to school and get Mr. Mwadunda—and how many Mr. Mwadundas must there be all over Africa? What can the child do if he doesn't understand? Or if Mr. Mwadunda doesn't understand? How can he ask his father or his mother, who is ignorant, who cannot read, who knows even less about school than the little child?

Then Bert was off about his university—how although the Asians were very bright in school, they just had no manners and just couldn't learn. Bring them to the dining hall or the recreation hall, and they would fall apart. They didn't even hold their forks correctly. Or they would always slurp their food. Or if a girl came into the room, they wouldn't even be able to speak, they would become all nervous and fall all over themselves.

And listening to this I couldn't believe that Bert who had been to the university could really be saying these things. It was so simple. Didn't he ever think it might be part of the Indian's culture, that they didn't learn how to hold a fork or didn't care if they slurped their food? Maybe Flakes didn't know how to hold a fork; who knows? But could anyone honestly think he couldn't learn if he was shown even once? Or about women . . . well maybe that was true, but it was because Indian women are not treated the same way as European women, they are brought up to cook and stay in the house and look after the men.

But he was going on—that they just didn't measure up. No matter how you sliced it, they just didn't measure up.

Then they were on about how lazy the Africans were. Try as you would with them, you just couldn't change them. There must be something in their blood.

Well, all right, sure they were lazy, the average, ignorant villager. But what about those kids, the way they worked? Getting up at six to do their calisthenics, working all morning and afternoon and into the night. Studying until three in the morning by the light of the kerosene lamp. Something in their blood. Ha.

But I didn't say any of this to them, I just listened. Maybe it was wrong of me, maybe I should have spoken up. But somehow I found it hard to do after the way they had been treating me. And the next week of surfing and swimming and genuine hospitality that I received there didn't make it any easier.

•    •    •

Welcome home, stranger, Jake said when I returned to Joburg. You told me you'd be gone just a few days, and here it's been nearly two weeks. Well, no matter, I have arranged a meeting with some of the African journalists that I know in one of the townships. I've spoken to them about you and they'll be happy to talk to you. We can go tonight.

So we drove into the township that night, down dirt streets like the township in Salisbury, with little brick houses along the road, about the size of ours at Ndumulu, each with a little plot of lawn, or a patch of dirt in front, with kitchen and toilet in the back. I wondered how many people lived in each house, maybe six or eight to a family.

We parked the car and I followed Jake inside one of the houses. It was just the same as ours at Ndumulu, the same three rooms, the living room a mite bigger, and with electricity, a bare light bulb hanging from the ceiling. There were about nine or ten Africans sitting inside, on chairs and on the floor, with two cases of beer, which Jake had bought, between them. Jake introduced me as we fitted ourselves in around the floor. More Africans were coming in, they would greet each other in English. They reminded me of the young officers in Tukuyu.

We began talking about the Congo, they wanted to know what I thought, how I felt about Tshombe and American imperialists killing their African brothers. About the murder of Patrice, who had gone to the United States for aid but had been turned down, and who had been scorned and denigrated by the American press.

And what did I think of this crime against the people of the Congo, perpetrated by the white man? And it wasn't just the Congo where the white man was committing these evil machinations. It was all over Africa—Rhodesia, Angola, Mozambique, here in South Africa where the entire African population was being suppressed. Surely I knew of Sharpville, of the fascist regime of the Nationalist party, of that butcher Verwoerd.

But they were training, they all knew what was going to happen. And it wasn't too far into the future. It was only a matter of time now. They had their boys overseas in Tanganyika, in Russia, in Algeria, even some in China and in Canada.

And I thought of a group of refugees I had met once in Dar es Salaam, which is the revolutionary headquarters for all the exiled liberation movements throughout Africa. How they would sit at the

New Africa Hotel drinking beer, reminiscing of the life in South Africa, disillusioned, disgusted with Tanganyika and Tanganyikans.

There was one of them whom I distinctly remembered, he had been a teacher in South Africa, he said, and now he taught in a secondary school in Dar es Salaam. Hearing that I was a teacher also, he had said to me, You know, if I can do only one thing in my life now that I am out of South Africa, it is to try and tell people, to try and make them understand how terrible it is to discriminate against a man because of the color of his skin. To try to explain what it feels like inside when you have to live in a certain area, when there are only certain jobs you can have, when they don't let you into a hotel or a restaurant—just because your skin is black.

And do you know, the worst thing is that after a while you find yourself beginning to believe that you aren't as good as they are, that you really don't belong with white people after all, that your children actually shouldn't be allowed at the same school with white children. And how can you fight it once you begin to feel that way?

Now one of them was talking to me, sitting next to me on the floor, his face right close up to mine. His name was Johnson and his eyes were all red and bloodshot, and he spoke in a very low voice, so I had to lean close to him to hear what he was saying.

I'll tell you what we need here, he said, we need three million African boys, three million of us, each ready to die . . . because there are three million whites here. That means one for one, each African killing one white man, one for every one of them, which means there will be twelve million Africans left. And even the way we are drinking here tonight, you and Jake, even though we are all friends, nevertheless you will have to die with the rest of the whites, even if you are O.K.

And it was a funny feeling sitting there listening to him say that —that I would have to die—with his nose almost touching mine, his red eyes boring holes through me. Involuntarily I looked around the room to see if anyone else had heard what he had said, and caught myself wondering if anything like that could really happen here tonight.

And I thought of Maggie, Jake's friend in that jail, and what she would be doing for the next five years—or maybe the next two or three if her behavior was good. How she was in jail just because she had disagreed with the way the Africans were being treated.

And I said, But surely you don't mean all the whites, not those who are helping you, do you? His eyes narrowed and he spat: All of them.

And I wondered then for the first time just what she was doing in that jail, if this was the kind of person she was sacrificing herself for. And I wanted to say, Look, you stupid bastard, is this what you really mean, what you really want, just to kill white people, even those who haven't done anything to you, even those who are actually helping you? Not caring about anything or for anything, except kill, kill, kill, anyone who is white?

But I didn't say it, I didn't say anything. I just sat there because there were two of us, Jake and me, and all of them. I just sat there looking at his red eyes, feeling his nose touching mine, smelling his beery breath, and thinking, Well, perhaps he is only saying this because he is drunk, and then thinking to myself that that was exactly *why* he was saying it.

Jake arranged for me to meet Morton Fertelberg the next day. He was a lawyer who belonged to the Liberal party. Would I like to go with him to a meeting—they met once a week—and then join him for lunch? He would be very much interested to hear my views on Tanganyika.

So I met him at his office—short, heavyish, going bald—smiling yellow teeth at me. He told me that the Liberal party was the last remaining link between the whites and the blacks, the only party left in South Africa where they still had interracial meetings and outside functions. It was Alan Paton's party, and in fact maybe he would be there today.

But he wasn't. Instead there were about ten Africans who looked as though they had just wandered in off the street, in dirty, torn clothes and shoes without laces, and about ten whites, all dressed in coats and ties, who looked as lawyerish and respectable as Morton Fertelberg. They were all seated in a semicircle, with a very studious-looking chairman, a white man in a blue suit and a vest. They all stood up as Morton Fertelberg came into the room and they said Hello, very formally, very stiffly, to him. Then he said, just as formally, just as stiffly, Hello there.

The topic for today was the Congo, the studious-looking chairman announced. And he read from a paper in front of him—

nothing I hadn't heard before. Then he asked for questions and comments from the floor, and Morton Fertelberg stood up and said that he had someone with him who was from Tanganyika and who would perhaps like to give his views.

But I said that being from Tanganyika didn't mean that I knew any more about the Congo than anyone else. Besides the Africans were all waving their hands frantically trying to comment on the Congo, so the speaker, realizing that I wasn't going to say anything, began to call on them.

They didn't say anything that I hadn't heard Africans saying before, from Tanganyika to the township. That is, that Tshombe must go. And if you asked them what would happen if he went, they would say, We don't know, but he must go. And then you'd say, But who'd replace him? And they'd say, Anybody, it doesn't make any difference as long as Tshombe goes. And if you said, O.K. but who'll govern the country? they would say, Look, man, as soon as Tshombe goes, the people, that's who, they'll govern the country. And then when you said, But they don't have any training or education, how are they going to be able to govern the country if none of them are trained, then the Africans would say, Look, it doesn't matter as long as Tshombe goes, that's the first thing. And sooner or later you'd become tired of hearing all this nonsense.

Except that Morton Fertelberg didn't get tired. He kept trying to argue or at least reason with the Africans, saying, But just stop a minute and think, or, But look here, why don't you. . . . And there were three Africans who were getting madder and madder at Morton Fertelberg, saying more emphatically, Tshombe must go. And finally in desperation Morton Fertelberg asked just why was it that Tshombe must go, why were they so opposed to him. And there was a momentary pause, as though they hadn't really thought about why he must go, they just knew he must, that's all.

Finally one of them blurted out, Because he is an imperialist stooge. And with that they all broke out in violent fits of guffawing, slapping their thighs and each other's palms. To steal and cheat the boys, that's what came to my mind, the staff meeting at Ndumulu. It was enough to make me start laughing myself.

But Morton Fertelberg didn't start laughing. And he was joined by his friend Irwin Something-or-other, and it was the two of them now against the three Africans who were screaming that Tshombe must go, that he was stealing and eating their rights and dignity and

217

freedom, just the way they were being beaten here—and I wasn't sure whether they meant the government in South Africa or here at this debate by Morton Fertelberg and Irwin.

Finally the chairman in the blue suit had the good sense to say that time was up. And afterward as we went to lunch, Morton Fertelberg and Irwin told each other that they knew it was hard but that they had to teach them, that was their purpose here in the Liberal party.

Then Irwin asked me if I had been successful, and I said, As far as what? And I don't think he knew what he really meant because he paused for a second or two, and then blurted out, In general, I mean—a little too emphatically.

And suddenly I found myself feeling sorry for these two middle-aged men, who were trying to put into words what they really felt, which was actually a good kind of feeling inside them, but that's all it was, I'm afraid, just a feeling, as though they didn't exactly know what to do about it, or they didn't understand it perhaps.

That night I went to Morton Fertelberg's house and met his pretty wife and three little girls—just by watching them look at him, you knew how much they loved him and thought him the most wonderful person in the world—and he was standing there, short and bald, so happy, so contented, almost cherubic.

Only I wondered whether he ever thought about that Liberal party meeting after it was over. I knew he wasn't thinking about it now. And I couldn't help wondering how much he really did believe in all this—whether he actually believed or just felt. Did he really believe in the equality of the African, did he really feel that they deserved the rights that they did not have here in South Africa? Did he really feel that they deserved the right to live where they wanted to, to have their children go to school with white men's children, to walk into any restaurant or any hotel—that the African deserved to be the equal of the white man in all ways?

Because if he did, if he really believed in all these things, then he couldn't sit here at his dinner table with his family cooing about him and feel so contented. If he really felt this way, then his place was not at the Liberal party, which was nothing more than a polite debating society, where everyone said hello to each other at the beginning and shook hands with each other at the end, and debated the Congo in between. No; as far as I was concerned, his place was not in South Africa, it was outside the country, getting support and training and money wherever he could, getting ready to fight when the time came, because that's what it was going to boil down to—there was no other way.

And yet how could I blame Morton Fertelberg and all the Morton Fertelbergs? It was one thing to have an ideal, a feeling. But just who was it, how many people was it, who did something about it, who really made any sacrifice? And moreover, just who were they making a sacrifice for? For the Johnson who wanted to kill all the whites? And how many Africans must there be who agreed with Johnson? Or was it for all the swaggering politicians of Tanganyika, or the officers in Tukuyu who got drunk every week-end? For those idiots at the Liberal party meeting who screamed, Tshombe must go, Tshombe must go?

How difficult it was to keep your ideals, your principles, when you saw the other side. How many times I had wanted to throw up my hands in despair at the staff meetings, at Bwana Mchanga, at the countless delays and disappointments.

But yet it wasn't for those people that you did what you did—why you had to keep on doing, why you kept on believing, difficult as it was. No, it was something more, I think. It was for the kids, kids like Fedson, those boys who got up at six every morning in the darkness to do their calisthenics, who worked all day, who pleaded for extra assignments—please, sir, can we have more sums?—and then on into the night with their kerosene lamp until three A.M.

•    •    •

Then it was over and I was heading north, back again to the Africa I had come from. Leaving Jake in Johannesburg, passing Jamie in Potgietersrus, across the border at Beitbridge, and up through Bulawayo toward Victoria Falls this time and into Zambia. Through Lusaka and north to Kapiri Mposhi, the meeting place of two worlds, white and black, where the tarmac continued on into the copper belt, but where the road to the north is mud and dirt.

So it was goodbye to the white man's world, the world of buildings and tarmac. And soon a broken-down Land Rover stopped and a black face was speaking to me in Swahili, and Yes, he was going north, all the way through to Mbeya—what a stroke of luck.

I'd heard stories of people waiting for days here at Kapiri for a ride. But he'd have to pick up some other passengers first, he would come right back for me.

It was nearly evening when he returned. He motioned me to come to the front, where there were three others, and as I walked over I saw that the whole back of the Land Rover was jammed with people, Africans. There must have been at least twenty of them there, lying over each other in all positions, feet sticking out in all directions, elbows at all angles, mothers with their babies tied around them, old men lying on their backs. And the smell, the smell, this must have been what those old slavers smelled like down in the hold.

And one baby was very sick, it was coughing very hard, as I greeted them all in Swahili. They were tickled to have a European riding with them, and some of them called out *Ndaga,* to me, Nyakusa, these people were Nyakusa, *Oogonile, oogonile,* I said, as we all laughed.

Then into the front seat, the driver had saved me a place next to him as I was European, and we were off, and he told me we should make Mbeya by tomorrow evening, driving all through the night, as it is five hundred miles from Kapiri to Mbeya. And the Europeans call it M.M.B.A., miles and miles of bloody Africa, because that's all there is, Africa. Only natives and huts and their villages, Africa.

The land is flat now with red clay along both sides of the road and large stones and potholes. And the rain begins as we joggle along, the short rains—they are just beginning now—and I think of that first trip to Ndumulu, last year, just about this time. How long ago it all seems. And soon I will be back there at Ndumulu, the beginning of a new year.

Night settles over us, and then the engine begins to sputter and cough, and suddenly the car has stopped. We go outside around the Land Rover while the driver fiddles with something inside the hood, as the rain drizzles on our heads there in the dark, as the men laugh and nod their heads to each other.

*Tayari,* the driver, says, Ready, and we pile back into the car and get moving again. And that little child is coughing still, very sharp coughs, and I turn around in my seat to look at it. The mother is trying to rock it to sleep, but the cough goes on, stinging out into the darkness, where the only other sounds are the rain brushing

220

softly on the roof, the little stones crunching as we churn over them, the occasional whisper of the Africans there in the back.

Suddenly the baby lurches forward and begins vomiting. There is blood mixed in with the vomit, all over the mother and trickling down the clothes of the two people sitting beneath her. As the car bumps on, the mother trying to clean it up, rocking her baby gently all the while—how wonderful they are with children—no one speaking, as though by not speaking, perhaps, the distance will vanish or the baby will stop its coughing and the vomit will all dry up and the smell will go away.

Sometime later I turned around again, they are all dozing back there, falling all over each other with a pair of arms or legs sprawled one way and a head another way. The baby is quiet now, and I am relieved, but I can smell the vomit that reeks through the whole car and I curse the mother and the poor baby. How am I to know that it will be dead before the end of the trip, that this is the reason it has been quiet now, and that the mother herself does not know, and still holds it in her arms, rocking it gently, thinking it is just asleep?

Later the driver stops the car. He is tired and asks me to drive, it is raining more heavily now as I slide across him to the wheel and slush the car through the dirt, which is turning to mud. But I smell something burning and I wake the driver whose head is bobbing up and down, and he tells me to stop. He gets out and looks under the hood and mumbles something, a leak in the radiator, it needs water.

But he doesn't want to fix it now, he is too tired, he says, we can sleep in the car and fix it tomorrow morning. Besides, he tells me, this is Serenje, where there are lions roaming about at night.

I don't really believe him, he is just tired, but what can I do except to curse him to myself and try to get some sleep? But it's not easy to sleep when there are four people in the front seat, with everyone dozing into each other, and I curse the driver again. But I cannot help smiling all the same, no one has to tell me where I am, only in Black Africa can this happen. I am back all right, back in the Africa that I know.

The minutes crawl by, it is all quiet now, only the smell, and I am even getting used to that. Twelve o'clock now, I am not really sleeping, just curling my shoulders around and checking my watch every few minutes to know when to start looking for the dawn. And wondering if there really are any lions around, and what I should do if one really does come. In that little car, alone there on the road—if I heard him roar, I would probably be so frightened I would just sit there and wait for him to swallow me.

But there are no lions or roars. And soon the dawn, and roosters crowing to each other, as I nudge the driver. He says we should get out and look for water to fill the radiator and gives me a pan to fill. So I go back along the road, looking out of the corner of my eye for anything that resembles a lion, and deciding every few yards which is the nearest tree I will run to, just in case he does come. But fortunately they aren't out this morning, and just as fortunately I can fill the pan from the puddles of rain that has fallen during the night.

Soon we are going again, but only for a few miles and then the smell again, and having to go out and fill the pan, and then filling the radiator until another few miles, when the smell would come again and we'd have to stop and go out and fill the pan again. And at this rate it will be four days until we reach Mbeya, so what I decide to do is to get out and wait for another car, knowing that it is the middle of nowhere, and that they have said sometimes nothing passes for days. Except that I can't take it like this, and besides I've had such good luck this trip, something is sure to come.

So I look in the back to grab my bag to say goodbye. And that is when I see the baby is dead, resting in its mother's arms, its mouth open, its face blue, the mother sitting there rocking it gently, not even knowing it is dead or not wanting to know.

The car with the twenty passengers minus one chugs slowly off, as it is just becoming light and now you can hear people moving about in the bush a few yards from the road. You can see their huts through the tall grass, and hear their voices calling to each other as they move along paths hidden from view by the high grass.

Then it starts raining again, a little drizzle, and then lo, there is a noise in the distance, a truck, a big one, coming from the south, and I go out into the middle of the road to wave it down—what luck, if only he will stop.

The driver jumps down from his cab, and we speak in Swahili. I can see that his cab is full, there are four people crowded together in there, not counting the driver. But he would like to help me, and I look up at the back of the truck, which is filled with oil drums and

crates and cartons, all covered by a long green tarpaulin. And I
know then where I am going to sit, right up there on top of the oil
drums and the crates, and I give him my bag and climb up on
top.

He starts his engine and we begin to move smoothly and quickly
along the dirt road. And I have to hold on tight to keep from falling, that's how fast we are going, as the trees seem to come up and
touch the sky, as the ground churns by beneath us, racing in the
other direction. And it is raining harder now, with a wind that
smashes the rain into my face, but we are moving, the world flying
beneath me, and I am heading home to Ndumulu. I can see myself
walking through the brick arch, the boys rushing to carry my little
bag, Fedson grinning, and the Twak peering at me from behind his
long black mustache and nodding his head, Very, very.

Yes, I think—Very, very.